SAFFRON

The story of England's red gold with delicious saffron recipes that family and friends will love

Sally Francis

Published in December 2011 by Dr Sally Francis, 21 Norton Street, Burnham Norton, King's Lynn, Norfolk, PE31 8DR.

ISBN 978-0-9550466-7-4

Book Design by www.drydesign.co.uk. Printed in England by Moreton Hall Press.

ACKNOWLEDGEMENTS

This book would have been impossible to write without the help of many individuals and organisations. I must first thank the Norfolk Coast & Broads Local Action Group of the RDPE for granting funding to my business Norfolk Saffron, including towards the publication of this book. I am indebted to the following for providing information, recipes, images, or original reference material: Carolyn Wingfield & Sarah Kenyon (Saffron Walden Museum); staff of the Norfolk, Cambridgeshire, Suffolk Record Offices and of the University Library, Cambridge, and the Forum, Norwich; Prof. José Antonio Fernandez (University of Castilla La Mancha, Spain); Prof. Pat Heslop-Harrison (University of Leicester); Steve Blacksmith (Halifax Scientific Society); Dr Debby Banham (University of Cambridge); Dr Allan Hall (University of York); Dr Carole Biggam (University of Glasgow); Dr Barrie Juniper; Dr Susanna Wade-Martins; Peter Mabbitt; Ruth Battersby Tooke (Carrow House Costume and Textile Study Centre, Norwich); Valentina Ravaglia (Dulwich Picture Gallery); Aviva Leigh (www.slowstuff.co.uk); Jean Thiercelin (Thiercelin 1809, France); Galton Blackiston (Morston Hall); Carla Philips; Anne Dolamore (Grub Street Publishing); Chris Coubrough (Flying Kiwi Inns); Kevin Mangeolles (Neptune Restaurant with Rooms); Dr Tim Kinnaird (Macarons & More). Credit too must go to my designer, Simon Dry (www.drydesign.co.uk), for his immense skill and also his patience. Finally I must say a huge thank-you to my family; they continually provide support, advice, help and (wo)man-power, all of which has been especially important this year.

Norfolk Saffron is supported by RDPE grant funding delivered through the Norfolk Coast and Broads Local Action Group.
The Rural Development Programme for England (RDPE) is funded by Defra and the EU.
The European Agricultural Fund for Rural Development (EAFRD): Europe investing in rural areas.

CONTENTS

PREFACE

I am an agricultural botanist. My saffron journey began in 1997, when my mother bought 20 saffron corms for my birthday. It was wonderful to harvest our first, very small crop of saffron. Although saffron was formerly grown at Saffron Walden, many books assumed it couldn't be done in England any more because the climate is now wrong.

Our little stock of saffron did well in the garden, with my mother diligently harvesting it each year whilst I was away establishing my career. Some years later, after several cycles of lifting, dividing and re-planting the corms, after starting a family and going self-employed as a consultant on 'alternative crops', there was more saffron than we could possibly use ourselves. We decided to sell some of our excess in 2009, and set up Norfolk Saffron. We have experimented to find the best strain of saffron to grow and overcome many difficult technical challenges. Our crop is now grown on a field, just like saffron was historically.

Only after growing saffron for about 10 years did I discover the extent of its former cultivation in North Norfolk.

Knowledge on saffron cultivation would have been commonplace over 200 years ago

In villages either side of ours, field-names still recalled the saffron crops once planted there. Knowledge on saffron cultivation would have been commonplace over two hundred years ago and we are rediscovering that knowledge all over again.

Whilst researching this book, I have had the pleasure and the privilege of reading original copies of valuable ancient books published during saffron's English heyday, and of conversing with the world's saffron experts.

This book, which has an unashamed Norfolk slant to it, is about dispelling some of the misconceptions held about saffron, about showing just how important saffron once was in England, and about encouraging its greater use now.

Sally Francis

21 Norton Street,
Burnham Norton,
King's Lynn, Norfolk,
PE31 8DR
www.norfolksaffron.co.uk

If you have any extra information on saffron's history, please get in touch.

THE PLANT

WHAT IS SAFFRON?

Saffron is a spice shrouded in mystery and confusion. Many people view it as just a glorified food colouring, yet it has so much more to offer than just the visual effects of its pigments. Good quality saffron, which has not been stored for years before use, also has the most wonderful flavour, not to mention potential health benefits too. Because saffron is still harvested by hand — it is a crop that has eluded mechanisation — it comes at a price. It takes 150-200 flowers and a lot of skilled hand-labour to produce just one gram of dried saffron!

Saffron can be bought as powder or as the whole spice, variously called threads, strands, filaments or stigmas. It is one of only a very few spices to be harvested from flowers — those of the saffron crocus, *Crocus sativus*, to be precise. The spice is often wrongly described as being the stamens from the saffron flowers. Others think that it is the pollen. But it is neither. Saffron comes instead from the female part of the flower. By convention it is referred to as the dried stigma (plural: stigmas or stigmata). Some botanists would perhaps more accurately describe saffron as being the 'style branches' from the saffron crocus, and reserve the term 'stigma' for just the particular surface at their tips that is receptive to pollen. Personally I dislike the term 'filament' applied to saffron because in botany the word has a specialised, narrow definition that is not appropriate — a filament is the stalk part of a stamen. With the 'stigma' versus 'style branches' question unresolved, throughout the rest of this book, the words 'thread' or 'threads' will be used for the stigma or stigmas/stigmata of saffron flowers.

SAFFRON'S SPECIAL CHEMISTRY

Highly concentrated saffron infusions have an intense orange colour, and with dilution, they give increasingly pale shades of yellow. The saffron threads contain a powerful pigment called crocin. This chemical is a carotenoid and has strong antioxidant properties.

Saffron gives a flowery, honey-like, yet slightly bitter, flavour to food. The unique

Previous page: Single open saffron flower. The part harvested is the red threads (the stigmata), and not the yellow stamens, as it is often claimed. This page (right): Serial dilutions of a rich orange, saffron infusion. Saffron's principal pigment, crocin, is so potent its colour is still discernable to the naked eye when diluted in water at one part per million.

flavour of the spice is due largely to the bitter-tasting compound picocrocin. This substance is thought to provide the delicate flowers with a defence against browsing insects. During the drying process, heat and the effects of enzymes from within the saffron's own cells break down picrocrocin to liberate the

Saffron threads contain a powerful pigment called crocin

aromatic flavour compound safranal. Safranal has high antioxidant potential and negative effects on certain cancer cells. Fresh saffron, plucked straight from the flowers, has a honeyed scent and it is only after careful and controlled drying that the characteristic saffron aroma and flavour develop.

HOW SAFFRON GROWS

Saffron is a perennial plant and so occupies the land for several years. In autumn, short leaves emerge from the bare ground of the saffron beds, and the mauve flowers quickly follow. In some climates, however, the flowers emerge first and the leaves come later. This unusual habit is called hysteranthous development. Compared with other crocuses, saffron is unusual because the threads are extremely long and protrude or dangle out of the flowers. It is one of a select few crocus species to produce a heady scent, making it very attractive to insects.

The saffron harvest happens just once a year, in late September to October, and normally lasts a few weeks. The flowers must be gathered daily before they fully open and the threads are removed and dried to become the spice, saffron. The threads are attached to the style, a structure whose colour changes from orange, through yellow and eventually white. In different commercial grades, and different producer countries' processing methods, the threads are picked from the flowers with either none or part of the style attached. This affects the strength of the resultant saffron; the more style included, the weaker the saffron. In other words, the styles are contributing to the saffron's

This plant, lifted in late September, shows the emerging new shoots, some leaves and one flower.

Close-up of threads/stigmata/style branches. Some brands of saffron contain large amounts of the style. In Iran, 'white saffron' is 100% style.

weight, without adding a lot of colouring and flavouring.

Saffron is exceptional amongst crop plants for its ultra-low harvest index: the economically valuable material (in this case, the saffron threads) expressed as a percentage of total plant weight, including the roots. In saffron this is just 0.5%.

Normally saffron flowers have six 'petals' (although in the botanical sense, these are not true petals but are tepals, we shall continue with 'petal'), three stamens and three conjoined threads. Just occasionally though, flowers with four, five or six threads are found. Swiss growers in the village of Mund call these flowers princesses, queens and empresses respectively. For each extra thread there is one extra stamen and two extra petals. With increasing numbers of threads comes increasing rarity. Empresses are said to occur at a frequency of only 1.2 per million flowers. As well as princesses, queens and empresses, saffron flowers can sometimes have just two threads, or very occasionally, none at all!

From the growers' point of view, producing flowers containing more threads is an attractive idea. But despite the best efforts of farmers and scientists it has proved impossible to either

Saffron flowers normally contain three lavish red threads that, when dried, become the saffron spice. Occasionally flowers appear with extra threads. Swiss growers call those with four threads 'princesses' and those with five, 'queens'.

breed a better saffron variety or alter the growing conditions to always get more threads per flower.

After the flowers are harvested, the saffron plants continue growing throughout the winter, producing long, slender, grass-like leaves, all the while building up stores of energy to see them through the following summer. The foliage begins to die back in late spring, and by April or May the saffron beds are bare again. In summer the plants are dormant.

Unfortunately, saffron cannot be grown from seed

Saffron can only be grown from corms. It cannot survive indefinitely without propagation by humans.

Unfortunately, saffron cannot be grown from seed. It is sterile and can only be propagated by planting corms (often called 'bulbs' by gardeners). If a single corm is planted, the following year it produces up to six daughter corms. These grow on top of the old mother corm, which itself dies. Every year the new corms develop closer and closer to the surface. Eventually the corms become overcrowded, small, and flowering declines. For these reasons, saffron growers lift, divide and re-plant their corms on a regular basis (annually to once every 12 years, depending on local tradition). This practice also prevents the build-up of pests and diseases, and it avoids exhausting the soil.

Older books often state that saffron's sterility is because it has been culti-vated for such a long time. The truth is that saffron is sterile because it contains three sets of chromosomes – it is a triploid plant – and any plant with an odd number of chromosomes cannot reproduce itself by seed. This disadvantage is offset by the fact that triploid plants are generally more vigorous, and the individual plant parts are larger, than in their normal diploid counterparts (with two sets of chromosomes).

THE ORIGIN OF SAFFRON

Greece, Turkey and Iran have all been proposed as saffron's original homeland. The plant is unknown as a wild species. It turns out that saffron is a natural hybrid, most probably between two Greek crocus species. Research work from a European consortium headed by the University of Castilla La Mancha in Spain has investigated saffron's origin and diversity using classical techniques and molecular biology. One of saffron's parents is *Crocus cartwrightianus* – itself sometimes called wild saffron – from Attica, the Cycladic Islands and Crete. In appearance, it is almost indistinguishable from saffron. It has a honey-violet fragrance and its flowers stay open at night. Its stigmata, though smaller than those of saffron, contain the same rich pigments. *Crocus hadriaticus*, an Ionian white-pale lilac species, seems most likely to be the other parent. But, *C. thomasii* (from Italy & Croatia), *C. mathewii* (Turkey) and *C. pallassii* subsp. *haussknechtii* (Iran, Iraq & Jordan) cannot be excluded from saffron's parentage.

It is supposed that *C. cartwrightianus* was

Saffron is a naturally occurring hybrid, probably of Crocus cartwrightianus *(left) and* Crocus hadriaticus *(right), both Greek species.*

the original source of 'saffron', gathered from the wild. What was the significance of it and another crocus species forming a hybrid? The answer to this question would have been nothing, were it not that the hybrid's flowers were larger and its valuable threads much bigger than in C. cartwrightianus. A special hybrid plant was picked out of a wild C. cartwrightianus population by an observant early farmer, then, as was so often the case in the early domestication of crop plants, deliberately propagated. This effectively formed the foundation stock of the crop.

It is not known how common hybridization between C. cartwrightianus and C. hadriaticus was, or is. Do all modern strains of saffron derive from just one hybrid parent or from many? Were hybrid plants selected more than once, in different areas, and at different times? The University of Castilla La Mancha research is tackling these questions.

In sterile plants like saffron, where sexual reproduction via pollination cannot reshuffle genes, genetic diversity is generally low and the plants look pretty much identical. However, there is variation in strains of saffron from different countries. This takes the form of differences in flower size, petal shape (lobed in Israeli saffron) and colour (a significantly darker shade in Sardinian saffron). There is also an unexpected level of genetic diversity in different strains. Possibly domestication occurred more than once.

For how long has saffron been cultivated? Its flimsy, short-lived flowers, and the delicate nature of the processed spice have left no botanical remains of saffron spice or plants in the archaeological record. However, saffron is depicted in a fresco of the palace of Minos at Knossos in Crete, which dates from 1700-1600 BC, and in a 1500 BC fresco at Aktorini on the Greek island of Santorini. Examples of documentary mentions of saffron in the ancient world are manifold. It occurs for example in the Ebers Papyrus (an Egyptian medical treatise of 1550 BC), in the Song of Solomon, in Greek myths and in the Iliad, and in Persian and Roman sources. By the fifth century BC, it was being grown in Kashmir, and in the following century Corycos, in Cilicia on Turkey's Mediterranean coast, was a major producer with an international reputation for its high quality. In these places, saffron was used in food, medicine, as a dye and for its perfume.

Saffron is depicted in a fresco of the palace of Minos at Knossos in Crete

One of the oldest names for saffron is *karkom*, which in turn gave rise to the Greek name *krokos* and the Latin, *crocus*. We have the Arabs to thank for the plant's common name, which derives from their word *za'faran* (yellow). They brought saffron to Spain in the tenth century. Saffron cultivation later spread over Europe, eventually reaching England. Derivations of the Arabic name for the spice occur in many European languages e.g. saffraan (Dutch), safran (French), Safran (German), zafferano (Italian), azafrán (Spanish), açafrão (Portuguese), Sáfrány (Hungarian) and Szafran (Polish).

Saffron moved eastwards. It was exported to China in the thirteenth century and to Japan by the seventeenth. Saffron was taken to the New World too. It arrived in North America with various European immigrants and is strongly associated with the Pennsylvania Dutch community. In the last few years, successful saffron growing enterprises have been started in Tasmania and New Zealand, and saffron cultivation is being promoted in Afghanistan as an alternative to opium poppies. In Europe, commercial saffron-growing has re-started in areas where the plant had all but been abandoned.

Spain is often thought of as the world's major producer, and although this was

After two centuries of absence, saffron plants are once again growing in North Norfolk, and the spice is once again available to buy.

once true, it has now been overtaken by Iran. All the rest of the world's production combined cannot now match Iran's, which churns out up to 200 tonnes of 'red gold' every year!

SAFFRON SUBSTITUTES AND ADULTERANTS

Nearly two thousand years ago Pliny wrote, 'nothing is adulterated as much as saffron'. With its huge hand-labour requirements, and consequent expense, many plants have been and still are used as saffron substitutes. As long as they are labelled correctly and not passed off as real, quality saffron, it is up to personal choice whether to use substitutes, but when substitutes are passed off as genuine saffron then that choice is unfairly taken away. Some saffron is impure, the weight being made up by adulterants. Many substances have been used to adulterate real saffron and trick the consumer. Stories appear in the press every few years, with a high profile case in Bradford in 2000 (Gangs make a fortune from the ancient art of adulterating saffron. *The Independent* 20th April 2000).

How is saffron adulterated? The easiest way for fakers to hoodwink customers

Bought in Istabul, this box of 'Turkish Saffron' shows saffron flowers on the label, but contains safflower (Carthamnus tinctorius). Dried safflower and the safflower plant are both quite unlike the appearance of true saffron.

is with powdered saffron. The kinds of substances mixed with the powdered spice have included various artificial food colourings, fine sand and even brick dust. Sometimes turmeric occurs fraudulently in powdered saffron; indeed turmeric is often suggested in recipes as an affordable substitute for real saffron. Turmeric is the dried, powdered underground stem of *Curcuma longa*, a member of the ginger family. It has a flavour all of its own, not at all like that of saffron. Turmeric brings further confusion when it is known by its alternative name of Indian saffron. To guard against buying impure powdered saffron, it is best to purchase only from a recognised, trusted brand.

Whole saffron threads are not immune from adulteration either. There are records of a huge range of substances, including dried meat fibres, pomegranate stamens, maize silks dyed red and scrapings of Brazil wood being added to saffron. Historically, evidence of such additions was provided by a very simple test: soaking a sample in warm water. All the fibres and threads present would rehydrate and swell to reveal their original shapes and proportions. A sophisticated and more difficult-to-spot modern scam is when genuine saffron that has been used already and exhausted of its colouring strength is dyed with red/yellow colourings and dried again for sale.

Pot marigold (Calendula officinalis) *became a commonly used saffron substitute by the seventeenth century for colouring dairy products.*

Many unsuspecting holiday-makers inadvertently buy safflower, labelled as saffron. Safflower (*Carthamnus tinctorius*), also known as bastard saffron, American saffron or dyer's saffron, is a thistle-like plant. The whole florets, comprising yellow and orange-red tissue, are dried for sale and look quite unlike true saffron. Crucially they do not give saffron's unique flavour to cookery. The extent of this problem is well illustrated by images on commercial photo libraries on the internet – searching for 'saffron' returns many photos of dried safflower!

Crocus longiflorus *is an intensely fragrant saffron substitute from Italy*

Pot marigold (*Calendula officinalis*), a common cottage garden plant, has also been used to give a yellow colour to foods. By the seventeenth century, in England at least, marigold petals (strictly speaking, the petalloid inflorescences) started to displace saffron from colouring dairy produce. (Nowadays, the colouring in cheeses like Red Leicester comes from a different plant, annatto (*Bixa orellana*), a species from the Amazon). Although it lacks saffron's colouring power and its odour and flavour, an advantage of pot marigold was that the plants are very easy to

Crocus longiflorus, *picked from the wild as a saffron substitute in Italy.*

Crocus nudiflorus *from West Yorkshire. Notice how the stigma is quite different from that of saffron.*

grow and they flower prolifically over a long season. Dried marigold does not look like saffron. To tell marigold petals, look for the little teeth on one end of each 'petal'.

Some *Crocus* species are, or have been, used as substitutes for real saffron. Wild *C. cartwrightianus* is still picked and used as saffron in Greece, and wild *C. longiflorus* is harvested by local people near Salerno in Italy. *Crocus longiflorus* is 'remarkable for the intense fragrance of its flowers, unrivalled by most other wild species'. Analyses show that compared with true saffron, *C. longiflorus* has smaller threads (but still three lobed and orange, and still containing crocin and picrocrocin), a slightly higher colouring strength than the lowest grades of saffron, yet a lower amount of the characteristic odour.

In England, a fascinating further example of a saffron substitute comes in the shape of *C. nudiflorus* (autumnal crocus, naked-flowering crocus or Halifax crocus). This introduced species has a curious distribution that puzzled botanists for a long time. It grows in West Yorkshire, Lancashire, Derbyshire, Nottinghamshire, Warwickshire and Shropshire, but especially around Halifax and throughout Calderdale. Only after painstaking detective work involving piecing together records of

The 'Halifax crocus' (Crocus nudiflorus) *in flower near Sowerby, Yorkshire. This fascinating species is thought to have been introduced as a substitute for saffron by the Knights of the Order of St John of Jerusalem.*

historical land ownership was a common link found between the main West Yorkshire *C. nudiflorus* sites. It turns out they were once owned by the mediaeval Military Order, the Knights of the Order of St John of Jerusalem Hospitallers. More recent research suggests 'an association in east Midlands sites with former Benedictine monasteries and the routes between them'.

It has been suggested that *C. nudiflorus* was introduced for medicinal uses in areas unable to grow true saffron, and was cultivated on a very localised scale. *Crocus nudiflorus* is a fully fertile species, able theoretically to set viable seed and it also spreads by stolons – underground creeping stems. It can maintain itself in the wild as long as traditional farming methods are continued. Conditions at the English *Crocus nudiflorus* sites perfectly mimic those of its homeland in the moist mountain meadows of the Pyrenees.

Saffron adulteration spawned the world's first food standards legislation

There is also evidence that *C. vernus* subsp. *vernus* (synonym *C. purpureus*) was used as yet another saffron substitute in England in times past. Two pieces of land near Beverley called the Crocus Fields still contained large populations of this introduced spring-flowering species in 1892, with the accompanying tradition that they had been grown for 'saffron' production. *Crocus vernus* threads are today used by French chef Marc Veryat.

Finally, some words of warning about meadow saffron, *Colchicum autumnale*. The plant is poisonous, not related to true saffron, and it should never be eaten.

The long standing problem of adulterating saffron spawned the world's first food standards legislation, the Safranschou covering saffron quality, in Nuremburg in 1358. The city was an important market for imported Mediterranean goods and dealt in huge quantities of the spice. To protect its reputation, punishments laid down in the Safranschou for adulterating saffron were truly draconian – those convicted were either burned or buried alive.

THE
ENGLISH
'CROKERS'

INTRODUCTION

Saffron is not a British native plant, so how was it introduced into England, and when was this done?

A popular theory is that saffron spice was used as an article of trade, and was first brought to these shores by Phoenician sailors seeking Cornish tin. However, firm evidence for this romantic and appealing story is lacking.

The Romans used saffron for many purposes, so conceivably could have grown it in their gardens in occupied Britain. However, saffron could have been imported, especially since the Romans thought that the best quality available anywhere in the world came from Cilicia in Turkey.

Some historians have proposed that after the abandonment of Britain by the Romans, the Anglo-Saxons may have carried on maintaining any saffron plantings that survived. The evidence put forward for this is twofold. First, Anglo-Saxon literature detailing the uses of saffron in medicine and dyeing, shows a familiarity with the spice. Second, derivatives of the Anglo-Saxon word *croh* (derived from the Latin, *crocus*), are claimed to be present in several English place-names. As an example, Croydon in Surrey, has been translated as meaning 'valley growing with saffron'. Unfortunately for this hypothesis, *croh* can additionally mean the dye-plant weld, and also 'a nook, a bend or a corner', so Croydon could just as well derive from the much less glamorous 'winding/crooked valley'.

Others consider it improbable that anybody took the trouble to look after old saffron plots during the politically unstable post-Roman period, meaning

Medieval saffron flower harvest. Saffron is still gathered by hand today.

the plants quickly died out. The small requirements of the Anglo-Saxon elite could have been served by imports from mainland Europe.

So assuming that saffron does not have a continuous history of cultivation from the Roman period, when was the plant first grown in England? A Tudor story neatly puts the date as 1339, stating that a pilgrim returning from the Levant risked his life to bring back a few corms in a special hollow compartment inside his staff. It is interesting that at least two other European countries have similar traditions of a single introduction event by one person. In Switzerland, a soldier is said to have introduced saffron and in Italy, it was re-introduced by a monk.

Saffron was first grown in England on a small scale during the reign of Edward III

Our English pilgrim's story is from a source written over two centuries after the event, so the facts and the exact date are considered contentious, although it is agreed that saffron was being grown in England on a small scale during the reign of Edward III in the mid fourteenth century. This was during an era of horticultural enlightenment, when several new plants (including rosemary) were introduced to gardens, as medicinal herbs, and the art and science of gardening was practised to a high level in England.

The saffron would have been painstakingly tended in gardens. Just as would be the case nowadays with a rare new species, we can suppose that supplies of planting material were initially scarce and very costly. The Revd William Harrison of Radwinter near Saffron Walden, writing in 1587, states that saffron became more common in the reign of Richard II, towards the end of the fourteenth century.

The earliest instructions in English on growing the plant are given in *The Feate of Gardening*. This treatise, whose original version could date to around 1340, was modified in the following century, perhaps in light of increasing experience in growing the many species it covers. *The Feate of Gardening* details how saffron corms were individually planted using a dibbler and recommends keeping the plots weed-free. However, saffron is listed in a section about 'the commodytees of Spayne' in the c. 1436 *Libelle of Englyshe Polycye,* implying that even after roughly a century of saffron-growing, England was still far from self-sufficient in its production.

Early on, saffron found a special place in monastic gardens, in particular amongst the medicinal herbs, because of its

Robert Kett's 1549 Norfolk rebellion against land enclosures made exceptions for saffron grounds. Tradition has it that the rebels met under this tree.

supposed anti-plague properties. At Norwich Cathedral Priory the plant was grown in the infirmarer's garden by 1461, and the monks not only produced enough for their own use, but they also sold excess spice and corms.

Saffron was eventually included amongst lists of herbs recommended for cultivation by every householder by Thomas Tusser in the 1500s. He thought that a 40 foot bed would provide enough saffron to satisfy all the needs of a lord's or knight's household. As well as producing a valuable spice, Tusser also pointed out that saffron's thick grassy foliage provided an ideal clean surface for spreading out linens to bleach in the winter sun.

Demand for saffron steadily increased, in no small part because of changing perceptions of its medicinal uses. Alongside this, horticultural experience and the availability of planting material probably improved too, and saffron made the transition from a specialist garden plant into also being a field-scale crop. By 1444 saffron was a titheable commodity, that is, being grown as a cash crop instead of just for home use. But moving from the protected environment of the garden into the conditions of the open field brought new problems.

Saffron's foliage, historically called *grasse,* is highly palatable to hares and livestock. This meant that the crop was only successful if adequately protected by fencing. The fenced areas were called saffron grounds, closes, gardens or (in Norfolk and Suffolk) yards. Instructions were specifically given to inspect the fences in December. This was the time during which the plants were most vulnerable to grazing, and grazing would reduce yields in the following year.

In 1549, Kett's Rebellion in Norfolk, a protest against land enclosure by the gentry, saw the widespread destruction of the many new fences on former open fields and common land. The rebels issued a petition containing 29 demands for change to Edward VI. Number one on the list was an acceptance of the necessity and expense of fencing saffron grounds, coupled with a plea that no new grounds be set up.

Saffron Walden in Essex is unique in England for being named after the crop

Areas planted with saffron and in the ownership of one person could be as small as one rood (equivalent to a quarter of an acre). Sometimes the plots of several 'proprietors' were fenced together as one enclosure. However, even when this occurred, the total area was still usually only 1-3 acres. As well as people either owning or renting land

and planting it with their own corms, landlords also let out saffron grounds ready-planted. In these cases, strict terms were laid out to leave the corms in place at the end of the tenancy. Sometimes payment was in kind. In Stiffkey, Norfolk, in 1573, '3 rodes of saffron ground' was leased for an annual rent of 1 coomb (4 bushels) of barley.

In countries with long traditions of saffron cultivation, the crop lends its name to towns that were centres of production: in Greece there is Krokos, and in Turkey, Safranbolu. Saffron Walden in Essex is unique in England for being named after the crop and was, in saffron-growing's heyday, the largest and most important centre for its production. It is thought this was because of demand by the town's many dye works. A charter of 1549, granted by Edward VI, displays a seal showing walls and towers surrounding three saffron flowers, visually representing Saffron Walden as saffron walled-in.

Around the town of Saffron Walden grew 'great store of saffron, whose nature, in yielding her fruite, is verie strange, and bindeth the labourer to greate travaile and diligence: and yet at length yieldeth no small advantage to recomfort him again', according to the

Representations of saffron flowers in Saffron Walden.

geographer and historian John Norden, writing in 1594. Civic records detail the costs of extravagant gifts of saffron to visiting royalty and dignitaries. Saffron flowers feature in pargetting (decorative plaster-work) on old houses, and in details inside the church. The town's pride in its saffron heritage is obvious today in the stylised saffron flowers in the logos of modern businesses and organisations based there.

A mistake in a botanical book published back in 1796, and perpetuated since then, led to a widely held assumption that Saffron Walden was the only place in England where saffron was cultivated as a cash crop. But this was untrue. Saffron's stronghold also extended into Cambridgeshire, Norfolk and Suffolk by the fifteenth century. Some years later, the number of Cambridge villages growing saffron would be astonishing, whilst in Norfolk, saffron seemed to flourish in the north of the county. Furthermore, saffron was cultivated in Gloucestershire and 'westerlie parts' according to Harrison, who thought it would also do well in the Vale of the White Horse (Oxfordshire) and the Chilterns.

Crops of saffron were remembered in field-names. Examples include Saffron Close (Histon, Cambs.), Saffron Field (Burnham Deepdale, Norfolk), Saffron Sands (Burnham Market, Norfolk),

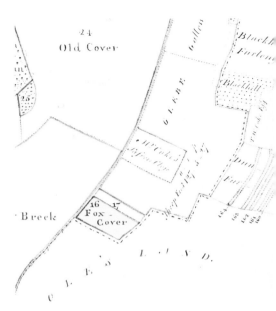

Burnham Market, Norfolk: A c. 1796 map shows a Saffron Close in situ (centre).

Histon, Cambridgeshire: A built-over former saffron close is remembered in this street name.

Saffron Rows (Docking, Norfolk), Saffron Pans/Panes (Finningham, Suffolk), Saffron Gardeyne (Holkham, Norfolk), Saffron Yard (Fornham St Genevieve, Suffolk). Documentary evidence of saffron cultivation also comes from Berkshire, Cheshire, Cornwall, Devon, Hertfordshire, Leicestershire, Northamptonshire, Oxfordshire, Shropshire and Wiltshire. However, by the seventeenth century, production had concentrated in Eastern England.

A second English town with a reputation for saffron production was Little Walsingham ('England's Nazareth') in North Norfolk, a town famous for its shrine. Though Walsingham could not rival Saffron Walden's production and standing, by the early years of the sixteenth century saffron was important enough to be listed in the wills of several Walsingham townsfolk. For example, Margaret Grey's will of 1516 mentioned grounds 'sett with safforne' and Edmund Heyward's, dated 1517, stated 'I bequeth and giff to Kat'yn my wiff... the closes of saforne, ye wiche I bought of Keswycke and Davy'. By the late Elizabethan period Walsingham, 'a

Little Walsingham, Norfolk. An important shrine and former centre for saffron production.

market towne of good accounte', was a place where 'groweth very much saffron & very good'. In 1755 Walsingham was still being noted for producing good saffron, as well as another specialist crop, the herb southernwood. However, after the turn of the nineteenth century things had changed. By 1847 no saffron remained at Walsingham and nor had it been seen growing there 'in the memory of man, whether wild or cultivated'. Perhaps as more research is undertaken, other forgotten regional centres of saffron-growing may be discovered.

THE SAFFRON GROWER'S CALENDAR OF WORK

Harrison and other contemporary sources go into such detail about saffron that it is not only possible to learn the traditional methods used for production, but we can also gain a fascinating insight into the social side of saffron cultivation, and even discover the specialist terminology used by the growers.

We shall begin our journey through the English saffron grower's year in early summer, just after the plants have entered their annual period of dormancy.

Although it is a perennial plant, saffron requires regular lifting and re-planting to stop the corms becoming overcrowded and diseased, and to maintain optimal flowering. In Essex and Cambridgeshire, Tudor growers, called *crokers*, lifted their corms after three harvests, whilst those in Norfolk and Suffolk waited until after seven harvests. In June or July, the corms (called *heads* or *roots*) from old saffron plantings were ploughed up or dragged out of the soil using a 'forked kind of Hough called a Pattock', according to Dr James Douglass in his 1728 account of the crop.

The land was next harrowed, then gangs of up to 15 people picked the corms up, loaded them into sacks, and took them back to the farmhouse. There, the corms were cleaned of adherent debris known as *rosse* and sorted by size. Any corms showing signs of disease were thrown away, as were the *spickets* or *spickards* – long, thin, unproductive corms. The largest and plumpest of the cleaned corms were used by the crokers themselves to plant new grounds, but excess stock was sent to market. Corm-sorting was also done by French growers, but slightly differently. They made separate stocks of wide, flat corms believed to produce more daughter corms, and rounder corms which were thought to be more prolific flowerers. In Italy, undersized corms are fed to pigs, and this might have occurred in England too. One acre of saffron was estimated to produce enough corms to re-plant an acre-and-a-half of new grounds.

New plantings were made on land that had not grown saffron crops for many years previously. The ground was meticulously prepared by multiple ploughings that often went deeper than usual, and massive dressings of manure were applied. Planting went on from June to August. Usually, the land was arranged in beds with paths running between them to allow access without treading and compacting the soil. The paths also served as boundary markers between different owners' plots, and as places for weed disposal later in the year.

It required 128 bushels of saffron corms to plant an acre

Labour at planting time consisted of teams of three: one man called a *Digger* or a *Spitter* and two women working as *Setters*. The Digger would make trenches using a spit-shovel and the Setters planted the corms. As he made each new trench, the Digger would at the same time cover the previous one with soil. It required 128 bushels of corms to plant an acre, though this varied slightly according to the market price of the corms.

Meanwhile, those saffron grounds which did not need lifting were described in 1771 as 'not at all regarded during summer, all manner of seeds growing thereon'. This weedy vegetation did not affect the dormant saffron, and was cut to make a kind of hay for cattle until the beginning of September. During the seventeenth century, the value of this hay could sometimes completely offset the costs of picking and drying the saffron. Hay-making on saffron grounds still occurs in Navelli in Italy, and there, the presence of the dried saffron leaves in the mixture is thought to be especially good for cows' milk production.

In early autumn, before the saffron's foliage and flowers began to grow again, growers had their one opportunity of the year to really get on top of the weeds. They needed to rid the beds of all vegetation and create bare ground so that, in Harrison's words, 'nothing may annoie the flower when his time dooth come to rise'. This was done by paring off the weeds using hoes and raking them into the paths to rot. However, it was vital not to accidentally damage the new saffron shoots (called *speers* or *spires;* described in 1771 as looking like the small end of a clay tobacco pipe) as they began to emerge. To get the timing right, growers would dig up a few corms and check for signs of re-growth.

To predict the yield of the forthcoming season's crop, Tudor crokers cut corms in half and inspected them. 'If they see as it were manie small hairie veins of saffron to be in the middest of the bulbe, they pronounce it a fruitfull yeare', wrote Harrison. Good saffron yields were also said to occur 'in that yeare wherein ewes twin [produce twin lambs] most'.

The all important harvest began in September or October. It was crucial to assemble enough hands to do the work in a timely fashion. Newly opened flowers last just a short while, and are easily damaged by bad weather. Conversely, they quickly wither in bright sunshine. Harvesting comprised two separate operations: *gathering*, which was the collection of the flowers from the fields, and the much more time-consuming *picking*, which was the removal of the threads from the flowers.

Gathering Saffron.

A view of saffron gatherers in Cambridgeshire by Nathan Maynard. Although saffron-growing had ceased when this illustration was made in 1845, local people could tell Maynard how the harvest was carried out.

SAFFRON GROWERS' TERMINOLOG

Blades or Chives = *Saffron threads or stigmas / stigmata.*

Cake Saffron or Saffron cake = *Sheets of compressed dried saffron, a speciality of production in England.*

To Child (applied to saffron corms) = *To produce daughter corms.*

Croker = *A saffron grower.*

Digger or Spitter = *Male worker who dug trenches for setting saffron corms.*

Dorts = *Flowers made by newly planted saffron.*

Dryer = *Person operating the saffron kiln to dry the spice.*

To Gather = *To collect the saffron flowers from the field.*

Grasse = *Saffron leaves.*

Heads or Roots = *Saffron corms.*

Hay Saffron = *Saffron dried loose.*

Kiln-burnt = *Saffron damaged by excessive heat.*

To Pick = *To remove the threads from the already harvested flowers.*

Rosse = *Papery covering of corms (tunic) plus adherent soil, dead roots and other debris.*

Saffron du Hort = *Saffron from first-year plots, highly regarded for its superior quality and reserved for medicinal use.*

Saffron Time = *The harvest period.*

Setter = *Female worker who planted the saffron corms.*

Shells = *Saffron flowers, especially after threads removed.*

Spickards or Spickets = *Poor quality, unusually long, narrow saffron corms.*

Speer or Spire = *Emerging saffron shoot.*

String = *Upper part of the 'style'.*

Yellows = *Stamens.*

A rental agreement of 1581 between one Norfolk landowner and his tenant specified, along with details of the saffron grounds and their treatment, that the tenant should have 'a place assigned within the house, if neede, for pycking' the saffron. The saffron harvesting went on daily, including Sundays, as new flushes of flowers emerged.

In very good years, growers could expect 20 lbs of dried saffron per acre

The gathering part of the harvest was usually women's and children's work, begun at dawn, and according to Douglass, usually finished by 10 or 11am. The flowers were gathered into baskets and brought home. On sunny days the picking went on outdoors but it was more common for the workers to sit around a table and do the picking inside. Nathan Maynard of Whittlesford, Cambs., recording in 1845 the recollections of fellow villagers wrote 'the picking of saffron was a time of hilarity and some strong beer was brewed expressly to be used at the time'. Saffron picking must have been a very social activity, with extended families and friends working together around their tables, discussing the prospects for their crop and the prices they might get.

Around the world, saffron processing (picking) is a highly social activity, often carried out by women. This scene is from Spain, but would have once been played out daily in farmhouse kitchens in England each October.

Notwithstanding all the beer-drinking, care had to be taken to remove only the bright red threads, in England called *chives* or *blades,* plus a short section of the style (*string*) from the flowers, and not accidentally include the *yellows* (stamens). The botanist John Parkinson wrote that the yellows were 'as unprofitable as the chives in... the wilde saffrons'. Flowers with extra threads were known simply as *double flowers,* but we do not know whether they had any special significance when found. In France, a double flower was called a *bessonnée.* Its discovery was, according to Jean Thiercelin, celebrated by kisses all round and glasses of white wine.

The empty flowers were known as *shells,* and had no value. They were discarded: 'throwne on the doonghill' or 'thrown away into ye street'. In Saffron Walden, the large volumes of spent flowers littering the town caused a nuisance recorded in its Court Rolls.

In very good years, growers could expect 80-100 lbs of wet saffron chives per acre from mature plantings, which gave up to 20 lbs per acre (19 kg/ha) of dried spice. Ordinary years would still see at least 12 lbs/acre of dried spice being produced. Yields were much lower on newly planted grounds established just a few months earlier, but Harrison says this saffron was specially set aside for its supposed premium medicinal value and

was called *saffron du hort.* Two hundred years later, the flowers of first year plots were called *dorts*, perhaps as a corruption of saffron du hort. The quality of the saffron changed subtly through the two to four week duration of the harvest. To make 1 lb of dried saffron required 4 lbs of wet chives at the beginning of the harvest, but towards the end, 6 lbs were needed.

Growing saffron left the land in good heart, probably because of the careful initial soil preparations, the high level of residual fertility from the manure used, the good weed control and close attention to preventing soil compaction. It was claimed that 18 or even 20 years' of continuous barley cropping was possible after saffron, with no further manure being needed!

DRYING THE SAFFRON

Nowadays saffron is dried loose, and may be marketed as whole threads or processed by grinding into powder before sale. A portion of the English crop was treated this way, to make *hay saffron,* which was afterwards stored in sacks. However, the crokers mostly prepared a peculiarly English product, not apparently made by their contemporaries in mainland Europe, nor by commercial growers anywhere in the world today. It was *cake saffron* or *saffron cake,* a dried, sheet-like compressed mass of threads, about ½ inch (12mm) thick. Although its quality was deemed lower than the alternative hay saffron, and it could be more easily adulterated with foreign matter like safflower, it was an easy way to conveniently store the processed spice. To make it, special mobile drying kilns were needed.

In the 1730s, the first professor of botany at Cambridge, Richard Bradley,

A unique speciality of English saffron growers was cake saffron, prepared in a special drying kiln. Picture by Peter Mabbitt.

recorded that most households in the 'saffron counties' possessed a saffron kiln, but that these were 'composed with very little Art', adding that their poor design and inefficient use caused much saffron to be spoilt during drying. Apparently, a common problem was the accidental production of 'kiln-burnt' saffron, caused by too much heat or by a lack of close attention to the kiln. The best saffron, according to a seventeenth century account, had chives of 'a high red and shining colour, both without and within alike', but poor quality stuff was 'oftentimes burnt, and in knots, spotted and mixed with the yellows that are within the shells'.

No known examples of saffron kilns now survive, but detailed contemporary descriptions give a good idea of what they were like. The standard kiln of the eastern counties was based on an oak frame, plastered over on the outside with lime and horsehair, and on the inside, with clay. It was square and funnel-shaped, about 2 feet high and stood on a base with short wooden legs. In the side was a hole where smouldering charcoal could be placed to provide the heat for drying.

There was some variation in kiln design. Walter Blith, writing in 1652, instructed that saffron kilns should be made of sticks and clay 'not half so big as a Bee Hive, and very like it'. In Shelford,

Cambs., one grower was using a cylindrical kiln by the 1770s. But if the harvest was poor, kilns were unnecessary. The saffron was instead dried between papers placed on a warming pan!

Probably the most comprehensive advice on drying is given by Bradley, but the method was little changed from techniques used much earlier. Bradley was obsessively keen on careful drying to produce saffron of the best possible end quality. His method was as follows. First two sheets of *saffron paper* – 'that is, a sort of paper made on Purpose for that Use' – were placed on the horsehair cloth over the kiln's mouth. Next, some small beer (beer of low alcohol content) coloured with saffron was used to wet the saffron papers, using a feather. The fresh saffron chives were arranged in a circular or square layer three inches thick (illustrating the huge amounts growers produced). More saffron papers were placed on top and a thick folded woollen cloth, topped by a wooden board, finished off the apparatus. The hot charcoal was then put inside the kiln.

Bradley's readers were encouraged to watch the kiln carefully until steam began to come through the upper saffron papers. Then, the saffron was turned over, sprinkled with small beer,

Bradley claimed that he had designed a revolutionary new saffron kiln

smoothed with a knife and the drying process continued. The saffron cake was inverted over and over again to ensure even drying. Lastly, when its thickness had decreased by three-quarters, a heavy weight was placed on the kiln-board to consolidate the cake as drying was finished off.

The actual drying process was extremely lengthy and often went on through the night. In 1599 Elizabeth Ransome brought a case of paternity against her former employer, a Mr Fiske of Binham, Norfolk. During the 'saffron tyme' the previous autumn, she alleged, Fiske had taken advantage of her whilst he had been tending his saffron kiln in his hall, and the mistress of the house had already gone up to bed.

In Cambridgeshire the dried saffron cakes were stored before sale by being wrapped in paper. Several of the wrapped cakes were themselves then surrounded by dry flannels, before being laid in trunks or chests 'not too moist or too dry'. The cakes would last 'a good many years'.

Bradley claimed that he had designed a revolutionary new saffron kiln and promised readers it would appear in his forthcoming book, the *Natural History of*

Essex and Cambridgeshire. Sadly, this title was never published, but Bradley wrote to Sir Hans Sloane of the Royal Society in November 1726, saying that he hoped his new kiln may serve as a useful pattern for people cultivating saffron outside Eastern England. Bradley was interested in drying saffron between sheets of glass, so glass may have featured in his new design.

As well as the actual cakes, there was another valuable product from the kilns and that was the saffron papers themselves – 'the Dryers perquisites', wrote Bradley – impregnated with the spice's rich colour and perfume. These were bought and used instead of the spice itself by many apothecaries, and were said to yield a fine saffron tincture. Sometimes excessive numbers of saffron papers were deliberately added to the kiln by the Dryers to maximise this source of income, but the practice was frowned upon because it reduced the strength and quality of the saffron cakes.

Dryers also had other tricks up their sleeves to increase their pay. They might knowingly under-dry the spice, meaning that a greater weight of saffron cake was made from the initial fresh chives, but such saffron would not keep and was 'apt to rot, and go mouldy'.

A third way saffron was prepared in England was as a tincture

Other fraudulent practices included greasing the saffron papers, which improved the appearance of poor quality saffron, or sprinkling the dried cake with melted butter to increase its weight. Both these could be detected by heating a sample over a fire in a silver spoon, or by the greasy, soft, flexible feel of the saffron when rubbed between forefinger and thumb.

Lastly, a third way saffron was prepared in England was as a tincture, that is, an infusion in alcohol. Amye Everard – the first female patent holder in English history – was granted a patent in 1637 for 'tincture of saffron, roses & c.' Tincture of saffron would, Everard claimed, remain in 'full strength and virtue for manie yeares more than saffron in the sheyve of leaf usually doth or can' and was 'more readie and easie for use than saffron nowe is or hath beene'.

PRODUCTION & MARKETS

John Gerarde's *Herball* of 1597 tells of saffron growing 'plentifully in Cambridgeshire, Saffron Walden and other places thereabout, as corne in the fields'. Around Saffron Walden during the Tudor period, astonishing quantities of saffron were produced. Harrison wrote that merchants buying saffron from the crokers inspected bags containing 'one or two hundred weight' of the spice. The overwhelming smell of such vast quantities of saffron apparently would 'strike such an aire into their heads... that for a time they shall be giddie or sicke'. These effects could last two to three hours, and also included excessive watering of the eyes. Some merchants tried to protect themselves against this by muffling their heads and wearing spectacles.

Famous saffron markets were St Ursula's Fair (later called the Common Fair) at Saffron Walden, held annually on 21st October, and Newport Fair (17th November). By 1736, Bradley discovered that Saffron Walden was no longer producing saffron crops, though growers from the neighbouring villages of Littlebury and Chesterford still sold their saffron there. Others, however,

Saffron trade routes from England to The Netherlands

Blakeney
Wells
Burnham
Kings Lynn

Amsterdam

Rotterdam

London

Veere
Flushing

Just some of the recorded shipments of saffron from Norfolk, 1580s to 1614. English and Dutch vessels were involved in this trade and the cargoes would be worth tens of thousands of pounds in today's money.

considered the market at Linton, Cambs., the best. Some records survive of unusual individual deals involving saffron, for example the sale of a property by William Taylor of Whittlesford Bridge, Cambs., for 3 lbs of saffron in 1673.

The papers of Nathaniel Bacon of Stiffkey, Norfolk, show that he sent home-grown saffron to London for sale, and records exist of at least one ship taking saffron from the nearby port of Blakeney to the capital. As well as the coastal trade to London, local customs records from the 1580s to 1614 reveal a foreign trade in which saffron was exported from various Norfolk ports to the Netherlands. No records of saffron imports occur at around the same time, so it looks as if the saffron (described as 'English saffron' in the Port Books) was locally grown. How long this trade went on for is difficult to say. Frustratingly, customs records are incomplete and only a small proportion of them have been transcribed into an accessible form. At times there were trade stoppages between the Low Countries and England. We therefore have only the briefest of glimpses into what might have been a significant business, involving English and Dutch vessels.

Large stashes of saffron were found in monasteries at the Dissolution

In the period 1610-1614, two ships in particular stand out as specialists in saffron export and both sailed from either Burnham or Wells. They were the *Estrich* of Veere, sailing to its home port, and the *John* of Wells which sailed to Rotterdam. They sailed into port with mixed cargoes, but significantly they usually made for the Netherlands carrying only carefully sealed wooden casks of saffron in their holds, presumably a reflection of saffron's high value. The *Estrich* was typically loaded with 20 lbs of saffron for each voyage. The slightly larger *John* often carried more and on 10th December 1614 left port with 60 lbs of the spice aboard. Even at the very lowest wholesale prices available globally today, this would have a current value of many tens of thousands of pounds.

Good and bad harvests, variation in demand, and sometimes also too many growers, affected saffron prices. There was a notorious period of overproduction in the mid 1500s around Saffron Walden, which afterwards caused a temporary collapse of the industry there. Growers complained that God 'did shite saffron therewith to choake the market'. Probably as a result of this, by 1572, the saffron tithe associated with the vicarage of Saffron

Walden had fallen from 50 lbs weight to just 7 lbs.

Trade was sometimes in the doldrums elsewhere too. In Norfolk, Dorothy Bacon wrote to her husband Nathaniel in 1597 that she had 'noe mind to sell your safforne', adding that prices were lower than the bottom limit he had set. A few weeks later she wrote again, saying that no-one had made any offers for the spice. According to Joseph Clarke (who lived near Saffron Walden, was a leading light in setting up its museum and could remember the last of the local saffron growers), the 'uncertainty of the crop and its vulnerability to bad weather' meant the crokers could sometimes be a miserable lot, developing an air of 'habitual discontent'.

Fortunately, since saffron does not deteriorate quickly, growers could in theory have stored their crop and sold when prices improved. Within living memory, Spanish families would steadily accrue a store of saffron over the years, only to be sold for example to finance a newly married couple to set up home. Back in England, during the Dissolution, proof of the monks' extravagance was claimed after the discovery of large stashes of saffron in the monasteries, bought as a way of storing great wealth in a small volume of space.

DECLINE, DISAPPEARANCE AND RE-INTRODUCTION

From its heyday in the sixteenth and seventeenth centuries, saffron cultivation slowly declined because of many reasons. Competition from imported Spanish saffron was a significant nail in the coffin for English growers. Saffron's popularity decreased in cookery, and

Saffron was included in some Victorian wild flower books despite having been abandoned as a crop. Detail from a plate of crocuses and irises showing saffron at the back. It is not botanically accurate, and was probably not done from a living specimen.

imports of new flavours — vanilla and cocoa — eclipsed saffron's roles in sweet dishes. Much later, artificial food colourings meant that saffron was never used in confectionery again. Saffron's medicinal properties slipped into obscurity and the invention of synthetic chemical dyes made it redundant in the textiles industry. It became more and more expensive to fence the saffron plots, and some historians have proposed that a fungal disease called 'the rot', which devastated production in France, also took its toll on the English saffron grounds. Eventually, a point was reached where the profits from selling the saffron no longer covered the costs of its cultivation, harvest and drying, and the crop started being abandoned. Saffron was already absent from Saffron Walden in the late 1720s, but clung on in the villages near the Gog Magog Hills in Cambridgeshire, as well as in North Norfolk, for several more decades.

Saffron was abandoned as a crop during the nineteenth century

Possibly the last recorded commercial grower in England was John Knott of Duxford, Cambs., remembered by Joseph Clarke. Knott grew around half an acre of saffron and travelled to London each year to sell it. By about 1816 he became too old for the journey and his neighbour William Thurnell continued until 1818. Saffron may have been grown for a little longer in the eastern counties; in 1823 'English saffron' was specified in instructions for making Spirits of Saffron. Knott died in 1827, in his eighty-ninth year. Finally, more than three-and-a-half centuries of continuous saffron cultivation in England came to a close.

Some Victorian wild flower guides included saffron, still present as a relic of cultivation in some of its old haunts. But without regular attention, with no fencing to protect it, and suffering constant damage by annual ploughing, the last remnants finally died out. By 1860, Babington's *Flora of Cambridgeshire* stated that the plant was 'lost' from that county. It is believed that none of the original English strain of saffron, carefully selected and maintained for so long, exists in the country today.

It would not be until the 1980s that the first fruitful effort to re-start commercial saffron growing in Britain began, on a Welsh farm near Wrexham. Meanwhile Saffron Walden Museum began to import corms for sale to interested gardeners. Then, after a decade of experimenting with saffron-growing, we set up our business — Norfolk Saffron — in 2009.

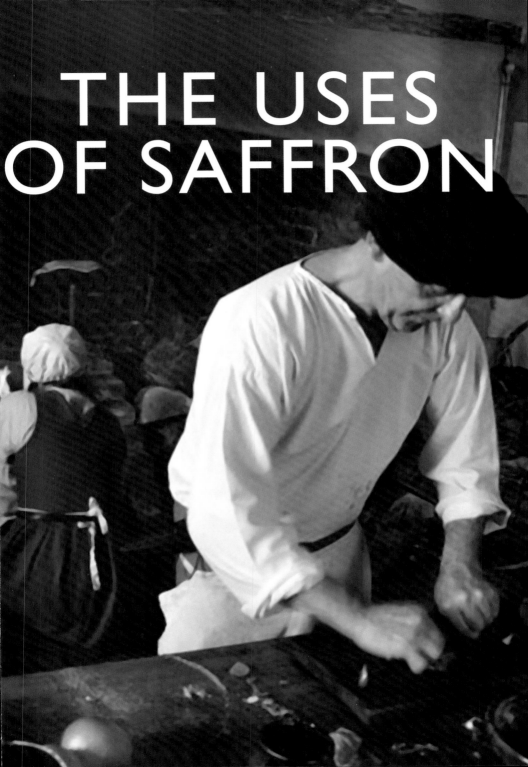

THE USES
OF SAFFRON

COOKERY

When good quality saffron is used in cookery in the correct 'dosage', food is imbued with saffron's warm glow and its special flavour. Somehow the yellow colour makes dishes instantly look more appealing. In this section we shall take a look at the many uses saffron had in the kitchens of Britain.

Pretty much the sole surviving traditional English saffron recipe still cooked on any scale today is Cornish Saffron Cake/Bread (or variations). Yet in the 1950s, saffron buns were still being baked in Suffolk and Essex. In particular at Thaxted, Essex, special oval buns were still being eaten on Good Friday. The Thaxted buns were made of a slightly sweetened milk bread dough containing cinnamon, grated lemon rind and saffron. Originally, Hot Cross Buns contained saffron as did Essex-made Simnel Cakes. A kind of traditional saffron bun recipe also survives from Co. Durham and from Oxfordshire.

It was during the nineteenth century that saffron usage seems to have declined most. Apart from things like saffron-enriched fruit cake, saffron's limited food use was only to colour some dairy produce, confectionery, jellies and liqueurs and as an occasional addition to white bread rolls ('a great improvement'). A general liking for saffron's flavour had vanished too. Rather than a national favourite, saffron became more of a regional flavour. Victorian botanist Anne Pratt wrote, 'in Cornwall... no tea table is considered furnished without a saffron cake. To most visitors from other counties the flavour is distinctly objectionable'. How sad!

In the 1950s, saffron buns were still being baked in Suffolk and Essex

We have to turn the clock back much further than the Victorians to understand how saffron featured in British food, and the following section gives just a flavour of saffron's many culinary uses. In the oldest of English recipes, saffron occurred in combination with many strong spices like pepper and ginger, in stews and broths. Many of these early recipes were influenced by the cuisines of countries from which the Crusaders had returned. Saffron's flavour may not have been apparent, though its brilliant yellow colour was obviously valued. Highly coloured food was popular in the Medieval period. Vivid green was provided by parsley leaves, red by sanders (the Indian tree *Pterocarpus santalinus*), and purple by mulberries.

In *The Forme of Cury* (c. 1390) manuscript, a recipe compilation of the master cooks of Richard II and one of the first cook books to be written in English, a significant proportion of recipes contain saffron. Richard II's court dined on food with strange and unfathomable names like Mawmenee, Chanke, Berandyles and Egurdouce, each often embellished by lavish quantities of spices. This is just one example from *The Forme of Cury*:

CHARLET

Take Pork and seeth [boil] it wel. Hewe it smale. Cast it in a panne. breke ayrenn [eggs] and do therto and swyng [shake] it wel togyder. Do therto Cowe mylke and Safroun and boile it togyder. Salt it & messe it forth.

As well as being an addition to the actual recipe itself, saffron was also

The Medieval technique of endoring – making food golden with a glaze of saffron and egg yolk. The endored biscuits are a rich yellow compared with the plain ones, plus they now have saffron's delicious flavour.

employed to make golden-yellow surface glazes on food. This Medieval technique, called *endoring* (from the Old French *endorer*; effectively, to make golden), was applied to items ranging from pie lids to roasted suckling pigs. To endore, the saffron was mixed with egg yolk, butter or almond milk and brushed over the surface of the food towards the end of its cooking.

Texts from the fifteenth century also call for saffron in a large proportion of their recipes. The *Potage Dyvers* manuscript of c. 1430 instructs cooks to use 'a lytyl Safroun', including in a recipe for meatballs of beef, pork or veal containing white sugar, cloves, pepper, cubebs and other spices, served in a sauce based on milk of almonds. The *Boke of Kokery* (1440) gives instructions on making Garbage – not rubbish as in the modern-day sense but offals, in this case a dish of chicken giblets. Take chickens' heads, feet, livers, and gizzards, it tells us, to prepare a dish flavoured with pepper, cinnamon, cloves, mace, parsley, sage, ginger and saffron. The *Liber Cure Cocorum* of 1420-40 likewise liberally uses saffron. Lines like 'Coloure thou hit [it] with safron' reveal that saffron's taste was maybe not of primary concern.

Items ranging from pie lids to roasted suckling pigs were 'endored' with saffron

Throughout the sixteenth and seventeenth centuries saffron maintained its place as an important spice. Harrison speaks of saffron's 'manifold use in the kitchin and pastrie, also in our cakes at bridals and thanksgivings of women'. Saffron occurs, with the usual ancient mix of dried fruit and other spices, in pies of minced beef or mutton and is in a late Tudor recipe 'to stue sparrowes'. In the 1596 *Good Huswifes Jewell,* saffron is in a list of 'all things necessary for a banquet'. The same book confirms saffron's use in the dairy: 'to make cheese yellow, they put in a litle saffron'. A delicious-sounding 'Tart of Cream' from *A Book of Cookrye* (1591) has a cream, eggs, sugar, ginger and saffron mixture cooked in a blind-baked pastry case.

Gervase Markham, in his *Countrey Contentments* of 1615, states that 'The Best Fritters' are to be made of apples coated in a yeasted batter flavoured with cloves, mace, nutmeg and saffron, and fried in beef dripping. In Shakespeare's *A Winter's Tale,* one line speaks of the need to have 'saffron to colour the warden [a type of hard pear] pies'. The saffron-plus-pears combination survived in traditional Essex cookery ('Always stew apples with cloves and pears with saffron') and is still used by chefs today. Another old source advises 'without saffron we cannot have well cooked peas'.

The Compleat Cook, published in 1658, uses saffron 'to dresse snayles', as an ingredient of a monstrous-sounding cake that also contains 12 lbs of currants, and in a sauce for eels. It advises, 'you must beat the Saffron to powder, or else it will not colour'. Meanwhile *The Accomplisht Cook* (1671) recipe for cheesecake 'in the Italian fashion' proves to be a multi-coloured feast for the eyes as well as the stomach. The spiced cheesecake filling, coloured with saffron, also contains pistachio nuts. After it has been baked, the instructions call for the top to be decorated with 'red and white biskets'. *The Accomplisht Cook* contains dozens more recipes featuring saffron, ranging from a minced eel pie made with gooseberries, cloves, mace, nutmeg and pepper, to heifer's udder pudding.

Admittedly the recipes above apply to high-status households that could afford books, and had literate people to read them. But in a time when ordinary people, in the country at least, were well versed with growing herbs and vegetables, their gardens may have contained a small plot of saffron just for their own use. They would not have wanted to overdose on saffron though. In France was recorded a case of chrysanthropy –

the birth of a golden-yellow baby whose mother had eaten too much saffron whilst pregnant. Harrison warns of the effects of bread containing too much saffron; those eating it 'become like droonken men, & yet otherwise well known to be but competent drinkers'.

Later, saffron was less often used with meat or fish. It gradually became common in sweetened breads/cakes, especially those associated with Easter (and in Sweden, with St Lucia's Day), and in cordials – distilled drinks containing herbs and taken almost as medicine. One example of a saffron cordial was Usquebaugh, a recipe originally dating back to 1695. This particular version is from Georgian Cambridgeshire:

IRISH USQUEBAUGH

Liquorice, sliced very thin, 1 oz
Sweet fennel seeds, 1 oz
Anniseeds, 1 oz
Coriander seeds, 2 drams
Best figs, split, quarter of a pound
Raisins of ye sun, split and stoned, 1 lb

Infuse for nine days in a gallon of good French brandy. Strain out and to ye clear spirit add ½ oz of ye best saffron, pulled out and tied in a cloth for 3 to 4 days.

The instructions 'ye best saffron, pulled out...' are revealing and imply that cake saffron was being used here.

I will finish this section with a snippet from Mrs Beeton. She wrote that milk was a 'good deal thinned with water, and sometimes thickened with a little starch, or coloured with yolk of egg, or even saffron; but these processes have nothing murderous in them'. The saffron would have gone some way to disguising the characteristic bluish colour of watered-down milk, but how revealing that saffron was used to adulterate milk... Milk must have been more valuable than saffron back then, a situation inconceivable today!

Saffron was extremely important in medicine, and occurred in preparations for treating a huge range of conditions.

THE MEDICAL VIRTUES

Saffron has a long history of medical usage, but this section must be started by issuing a disclaimer. Please do not read the following information and decide to self medicate with saffron – instead consult your GP!

The earliest medical works in Britain contained much information gleaned from Greek, Roman and even Arab sources. The Roman work of Apicius contains instructions for making Salts for Many Ills, adding 'they are very gentle indeed and more healthful than you would expect'. Saffron was a key ingredient.

Saffron is also mentioned in Anglo-Saxon medical literature. In a fifth century remedy for diseases of the mouth and throat, saffron is paired with the bile of a wild goat. Saffron is also listed in the tenth century *Leechbook of Bald*. Much later, saffron was thought essential for treating the plague, and some say this is why it was introduced into England in the first place.

No-one can perhaps match the saffron-enthusiasm of German physician Johann Ferdinand Hertodt. In 1671 he published *Crocologia*, a book entirely about saffron's medical virtues. We have a rich vein of medicinal information from the works of leading sixteenth and seventeenth century English physicians too.

The English herbalists John Gerarde (writing in 1597) and Nicholas Culpeper (mid seventeenth century), as well as the account of saffron by Harrison (1587), provided detailed information on saffron in medicine.

Gerarde states that overmuch saffron consumption produces a headache, and interferes with sleep. Culpeper, writing a few years later, warned that after saffron overdose 'some have fallen into an immoderate laughter, which ended in death'. Cases of fatalities have indeed been recorded after huge doses of saffron have been eaten.

Moderate use of saffron was considered good for the brain

Moderate use of saffron was considered good for the brain, making the senses quicker and more lively. Saffron strengthened the heart and benefited the digestion. It was excellent for sufferers of consumption of the lungs and for those 'at deaths doore & almost past breathing'. Saffron was used to treat liver and gallbladder problems, especially jaundice. To illustrate the often blurred boundary between medicine and food, here is a 17th century remedy:

For the yellow jaundisse, take two penny-worth of the best English saffron, drie it and grinde it to an exceeding fine powder, then mix it up with the pap of a rosted apple, and give it to the diseased party to swallow downe in the manner of a pill... without doubt it is the most present cure that can be for the same, as hath beene often proved.

For those with bladder problems, saffron provoked urination, helped expel bladder stones and gave 'no small ease to them that make their water by dropmeales'. Saffron 'mingled with the milke of a woman and laied upon the eyes' removed the 'red wheales and pearls that oft grow about them' and saffron infusions in other fluids protected the eyes against damage caused by smallpox or measles. Saffron was good for those suffering from deafness, smallpox, St Anthony's fire and shingles.

Against the pestilence (plague), saffron was of prime importance. Gerarde's medicine for this disease contained walnuts, figs, 'mithridate', sage leaves, 'pimpernell water' and saffron. It 'preserveth from the pestilence and expelleth it from those that are infected'.

Saffron had an important role as a herb for women. It was given to promote menstruation, to speed childbirth and delivery of the placenta, and for 'female obstructions'. The large doses used in its darker side as an abortifacient came with a high risk of death to the mother.

Anti-depressant properties were recognised in saffron. The saying 'Domirit in sacco croci' – he hath slept in a bag of saffron – alluded to someone of a merry disposition. Gerarde wrote that saffron 'maketh a man merrie'. A recipe for 'Melancholy Water' from 1672 contains 'three peniworth of Saffron' as well as the flowers of clove carnations, Damask roses, rosemary, marigold and borage, along with other herbs and spices. The mixture was distilled; 'Leaf-Gold' and sugar was added. As well being a presumed anti-depressant preparation, Melancholy Water was also 'good for Women in Child-bed if they are faint'.

Even the smell of saffron had medicinal value. It was worn in small bags under the chin of those suffering from smallpox and also to relieve the symptoms of seasickness.

Saffron had some reputation as an aphrodisiac. 'It is with good successe given to procure bodily lust', wrote Gerarde. A century earlier, Platina in his book *De Honesta Voluptata et Valetudine* said that eating his Saffron Dish – a sugary, almond, chicken, eggs and saffron concoction – 'stirs passion'.

Finally, the mysterious medicinal ingredient hermodactyls were, Culpeper thought, merely the dried roots of saffron plants.

Some medicinal and culinary recipes called for Spirits of Saffron, not the same as the Tincture of Saffron mentioned on page 32. From 1823 came the following instructions:

SPIRITS OF SAFFRON

Pick eight ounces of English saffron very clean, cut it fine, and steep it twenty-four hours in a gallon of the best white wine. Put it into an alembic [a still] with three gallons of water, draw it off gently so long as the saffron tastes, and sweeten it with white sugar candy. Dissolve the candy in some of the weaker extract, after the stronger part is drawn off, by setting it on the fire, and then mix the whole together.

A few Victorian remedies included saffron, for example the Antispasmodic

Saffron was worn in small bags under the chin of those suffering from smallpox

Tea described by Charles Francatelli in *A Plain Cookery Book for the Working Classes* (1852), was a treatment for indigestion. However, by the late 1880s saffron was only employed by pharmacists as a colorant, rather than for recognised medicinal properties.

Up until the 1950s saffron tea was a common home-made remedy for measles (recorded from Felixstowe and Mellis, both in Suffolk) and at Mellis, saffron tea was given in small doses to canaries to keep their plumage yellow. Although no longer used in mainstream medicine, saffron still has a place in modern herbal preparations. It is used to treat depression and menstrual disorders.

Up until the 1950s saffron tea was a common home-made remedy for measles

How do saffron's ancient medicinal uses stand up to scientific scrutiny? Modern findings, some using human subjects, some in animals and some *in vitro,* using either whole extracts from saffron, purified saffron compounds, or crocin sourced from other plants, were reviewed in the scientific literature in 2010 by a team from the University of Guelph, Canada.

Saffron had positive effects on gastric ulcers in studies on rats. In mice, saffron increased gastric acid and pepsin production, showing the potential of saffron to improve the digestion of proteins.

It has been long suggested that the low incidence of heart disease in Spain is due to regular consumption of saffron. Studies using animal subjects show that crocin purified from saffron reduces blood cholesterol levels, meaning it could have a role in promoting heart health.

In cases of depression, positive effects on human subjects were gained by using saffron threads extract. Saffron petal extract was similarly effective. The petals' active ingredient is kaempferol, a substance with known antidepressant effects. Petal extracts also helped alleviate the emotional symptoms associated with premenstrual syndrome.

An especially exciting field of research is saffron's effects on various cancers. Experiments have been carried out on breast, cervical and liver cancer cell lines grown *in vitro,* showing that purified saffron compounds prevent cancer cell proliferation and/or are toxic to the cancer cells. More studies are needed to ascertain the whole spice's effects on cancers using human subjects.

In addition to the above, research from the University of L'Aquila in Italy recently demonstrated that saffron has beneficial effects on the eye. Though the work is still at a preliminary stage, early indications are that saffron might act against age-related macular degeneration, retinitis pigmentosa, and generally make the cells involved in vision much better at coping with bright sunlight.

More research, using larger numbers of human subjects, is required, but a better understanding of saffron's medicinal value is something to look forward to in the future. Who knows, more of saffron's old uses may be verified.

SAFFRON AS A DYE AND PIGMENT

Saffron has been used as a dye since antiquity. Typically, natural dyes require the fibres, yarn or fabric to be first treated with a mordant. The mordant (the most common one being alum) fixes the dyestuff and prevents it being washed out. Saffron, however, is special. It is a 'substantive dye' that needs no mordanting.

The past participle *gecroged* – meaning 'saffroned', coloured by saffron – occurs in Anglo-Saxon literature. Small luxury items could have been dyed

Baconsthorpe Castle, Norfolk. From 1560, industrial-scale textiles manufacturing took place in the central buildings in this photo. This included dyeing - perhaps with locally produced saffron.

with saffron during this period, most probably with imported saffron. Saffron was later used for colouring the clothes of the kings of Ireland. Henry VIII confined saffron to dyeing garments of the nobility.

Dyers whose colours were more brilliant and intense than their competitors owned very valuable intellectual property. They typically jealously guarded their recipes, so there is little concrete evidence to go on when researching this side of saffron's history. However, the seventeenth century Cambridge academic

Saffron was used for colouring the clothes of the kings of Ireland

John Ray wrote that Irish women dyed their clothes with saffron because of its reputation for strengthening the limbs, adding, 'they say that our sailors do the same'. Modern techniques have shown the presence of saffron in fabric samples.

Saffron's East Anglian centre of cultivation was also one of England's most important wool and cloth manufacturing areas. Of particular importance was Norwich, England's only provincial city with its own Cloth Halls for the measuring and taxation of textiles. Norwich also contained its

Saffron-dyed cotton, linen, silks and felt, made by Aviva Leigh using Norfolk Saffron.

communities of Strangers – Dutch and Walloon immigrants invited in the 1560s to settle in the city and share their weaving expertise. This resulted in innovative, more colourful textiles being produced.

English court fashion in c. 1615. Golden lace ruffs and cuffs, and low-cut bodices, provoked intensely moralised reactions and confirmed the Puritans' stereotyped ideas about the excesses of court life. The golden colour here was probably provided by yellow starch made using saffron.

Industrial-scale textiles manufacturing was also carried out in rural areas close to saffron-growing villages, for example by the Heydon family of Baconsthorpe in North Norfolk. Parts of their home, Baconsthorpe Castle, a fortified manor house, were developed into a textiles factory in around 1560. The estate's 'integrated farming and manufacturing enterprise' had flocks of sheep numbering 20,000 - 30,000, whilst the Castle had its own fulling mill, special rooms with large windows where weavers worked at their looms and possibly also a dye-house. The Heydons grew rich on trading cloth, some of which was probably exported from the nearby port of Blakeney.

Certainly there was potential for large scale saffron usage by the vibrant local textiles industry, but it seems in Norfolk that an alternative source of yellow, weld (*Reseda luteola*), was also in cultivation at the same time as saffron. Weld grows easily, almost like a weed, quite unlike the much more fussy saffron. All of weld's foliage and stems yield dye, compared with just the tiny threads in saffron. To what extent the bombazines, callimancoes, dornixes, mocadoes, quadramids and other Norwich textiles of the sixteenth and seventeenth centuries, or the fabrics made elsewhere in England, used saffron or weld, it is probably impossible now to say. A key point may have been differences in the quality and precise hue of yellow given by each plant, plus the relative value of the fabric being produced.

One case where we do have positive evidence for dyeing with saffron is in yellow starch. Anne Turner, widow of a favourite of Elizabeth I, invented yellow starch – a starch plus saffron mixture – for anointing and colouring stiff lace ruffs. The fashion for yellow starched ruffs was eagerly taken up by Anne of Denmark, Queen of James I, and became hugely popular at court. It was

The colour yellow had associations with pride and lust

not without its criticisms though. To us, it seems strange that a colour could provoke an intensely moralised reaction, but this is exactly what happened in Stuart England. The reason was that yellow had associations with fertility in the unmarried, sexual jealousy in the married and also with pride and lust. Unnaturally large, stiff yellow ruffs coupled with risqué, very low-cut bodices served only to confirm the Puritans' stereotypes about the excesses of James I's court.

Anne Turner became implicated as an

Weld, one of several other species to yield yellow dye. Field crops of weld were grown around the same time as saffron, so both plants could have been used by dyers.

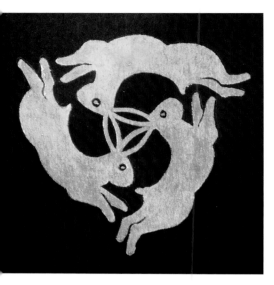

Our attempt at re-creating the false gold leaf technique of the Middle Ages. The image was first painted in silver, then over-painted with a mixture of saffron and 'glair' – the liquid that collects under partially beaten egg white.

accessory to murder in a case known as the Overbury Affair, which led to her execution in 1615, and whipped up more negative feelings towards yellow ruffs. The Overbury Affair was a huge scandal at the time, involving the poisoning of Sir Thomas Overbury, adultery and alleged witchcraft. After her hanging, Mistress Turner was described very caustically as 'an arrant whore or bawd, and the first that brought up the fashion for yellow starch'. Although the scandal tainted the image of yellow starch, it would continue to be used on ruffs. In March 1620 it was noted that the Dean of Westminster had been very strict in his church against 'ladies and gentle-women' wearing yellow ruffs and

Silk yarn and fabric in a saffron dye-bath, made by Aviva Leigh using Norfolk Saffron.

would not allow them to be admitted to any pew.

Norwich-based artisan textiles maker, Aviva Leigh (www.slowstuff.co.uk), has made dyeing experiments with Norfolk Saffron as well as with weld and turmeric. The intensity of colour produced by the saffron is astonishing. On silk, the saffron is especially brilliant and gives a very golden yellow, 'like sunshine', in her words. Saffron is also taken up well by linen, where the shade has a hint of pink in it. Weld's and turmeric's yellows are good, but different. Natural dyes are attracting interest for their environmental credentials, which can only breathe new life into saffron's ancient role as a provider of yellow colour.

On silk, saffron is especially brilliant and gives a very golden yellow

Saffron's pigments were used for colouring things other than food and textiles. The Medieval monk Theophilus, writing in the twelfth century, carefully explains how powdered saffron 'with which silk is dyed' and powdered tin were used in manuscripts to create fake gold leaf. The Ancient Egyptians' technique of 'writing in gold, without gold' required saffron mixed with terrapin bile. Saffron itself was probably also used as

Pure sunshine: silk yarn dyed with saffron, made by Aviva Leigh using Norfolk Saffron.

a yellow in its own right. The following is a pigment recipe from the Elizabethan period:

Take an ounce of Orpiment [the yellow compound, arsenic sulphide], one ounce of fine Christall, braye them severallie, and mingle with them the white of an Egge.

Take Saffron dryed, beaten into powder, and put to it as much glittering Orpiment that is scaly and not earthie, then with the gall of an Hare or a Pyke, braye them togeather, put them in some violl under a dunghill five daies, then take it out and keep it, for it is the colour of Golde.

A hair dye recipe from 1694 uses ceruse, lime and saffron to get a blonde colour

prevent the dye from staining the insides'. The same book has a belt-and-braces approach to providing sufficient yellow pigment in its Varnish for Brass recipe by including three yellow spices – saffron, turmeric and annatto. The resultant varnish, 'when applied to rails for desks, has a most beautiful appearance, like that of burnished gold'.

A hair dye recipe from 1694 uses ceruse (white lead mixed with vinegar), lime and saffron to get a blonde colour.

Even until the early years of the nineteenth century, saffron was being recommended as a household source of yellow or golden colour. *The Cook and Housekeeper's Complete and Universal Dictionary* (a late Georgian book) uses a saffron infusion to clean and restore a yellow colour to fine leather gloves. It warns to sew the gloves up before the treatment, 'to

SAFFRON
RECIPES

NOTES ON USING SAFFRON

There are three key points to success when cooking with saffron. First, the saffron needs to be of good quality and fresh. Before making the following recipes, throw out any dusty old saffron that has been languishing at the back of your cupboard and buy some fresh stuff – you'll be amazed at the aroma! Second, the correct amount needs to be used; too much is not pleasant, too little means it's overwhelmed by other ingredients. Third, saffron needs time to give up its colour and flavour.

Assuming threads are being used, steep them in a hot or warm liquid – water, milk, wine and stock are all fine (liquids containing alcohol or fat are said to extract additional, non-water-soluble pigment compounds from the saffron). Leave to infuse for at least 20 minutes before adding to the rest of the recipe. More colour and flavour is extracted if the threads are crumbled before infusion. This gives food a background yellow colour with hotspots of reddish-orange. For maximum colour and flavour, and to make the saffron go furthest, grind it in a pestle and mortar before infusing. This uniformly colours the food yellow. If the saffron 'glazes' on the inside of the mortar, remove it by adding some of the infusing liquid and rubbing around with the pestle. I generally use saffron after crumbling or grinding it first.

Saffron quantities can be expressed as either a 'pinch', a number of threads (my favourite method), fractions of a teaspoon full or fractions of a gram. All ways work fine, although the first time you cook a recipe with a pinch of saffron, err on the side of caution and put in a small pinch. You can always add more saffron later on if the flavour is too weak for you.

For those wishing to develop their own recipes, saffron goes well with: vanilla; cardamom; pineapples; oranges; apples; pears; peaches or apricots; white chocolate; leeks and onions; any sea fish or shellfish, but especially mussels; and chicken. In desserts and baking, saffron can often be used instead of vanilla.

In choosing the recipes for this book, I have deliberately not just reproduced obvious saffron dishes like Paella or Cornish Saffron Cake. These occur in many cook books. Instead I have tried to show the diversity of ways saffron can be used by including a wide range of dishes, some of which you may never have thought of using saffron in. The following are things we cook at home, recipes from other saffron books, and special contributions from expert chefs working near us in Norfolk. Ideally please make them with Norfolk Saffron, but any other quality brand is fine!

HARICOTS À LA GRECQUE

Modified from Jean Thiercelin's wonderful book *Saffron: The Gold of Cuisine* (Agnès Viénot Éditions: 2008). The Thiercelin family, based in France, have been trading saffron for over two centuries. Jean Thiercelin is the sixth generation in the oldest saffron and sales business in the world.

INGREDIENTS FOR 4 SERVINGS

¼ g saffron threads
juice of one lemon
1 spring onion, chopped
300g olive oil

250g dry white haricot beans
salt
Esplette pepper or cayenne pepper

METHOD

- The night before, cover the beans with cold water and leave to soak overnight.

- The next day, drain the beans and put them into a large saucepan. Cover them with a generous amount of cold water and bring to the boil. When the beans are three-quarters cooked, add salt. Continue cooking, check for doneness and drain the beans.

- Grind the saffron in a mortar and steep in 1 tbsp of the lemon juice for at least 20 mins.

- Blend the cooked beans with the lemon juice, saffron and chopped spring onion. Whisk in the oil.

- Garnish with Esplette or cayenne pepper.

- This purée may be used cold as a dip, or may be served warm with any fish dish, or with pigeon or duck.

Note on metric and Imperial measurements
Imperial measurements have been left in place if provided, but some recipes were developed using only metric and are tricky to accurately convert.

VELOUTÉ OF MUSSELS WITH SAFFRON AÏOLI

By Galton Blackiston, Morston Hall, Norfolk. He writes, 'I know I'm biased, but I do believe the mussels gathered at Morston are the plumpest and tastiest you can get. The only down side is that they do need a bit of work, scraping off all the barnacles. They are best left in the fridge overnight in a bowl of lightly salted water with plain flour scattered over (ingesting the flour encourages the mussels to spit out any sand and grit).' Before you cook them, discard any mussels that that stay open even after giving them a few sharp taps on their shells.

INGREDIENTS FOR 6 SERVINGS

SAFFRON AÏOLI

1 egg
2 tbsp lemon juice
2 tsp Dijon mustard or
   1 tsp English mustard powder
2 cloves of garlic, finely grated

a good pinch of saffron threads
   infused in:
1 tbsp hot water and allowed to cool
300ml (½ pint) sunflower oil
salt and pepper

VELOUTÉ OF MUSSELS

1kg (2lb 4oz) mussels, scraped,
   de-bearded and cleaned
225ml (8fl oz) white wine
50g (2oz) butter
1 medium onion, peeled and
   finely sliced
2 tsp plain flour

1 tsp medium curry powder
150ml (¼ pint) fish or chicken stock
150ml (¼ pint) double cream
1 x 120g pack of baby spinach leaves,
   washed
6 tsp snipped chives, to garnish

METHOD: SAFFRON AÏOLI

- Place the egg and lemon juice into the bowl of a food processor together with the mustard, garlic, saffron and a good seasoning of salt and pepper. Whizz on a high speed; turn off the machine and using a spatula scrape down the sides and bottom of the bowl to make sure everything gets properly incorporated. Turn the machine back on and very slowly drizzle in the sunflower oil; the mixture will emulsify and then thicken. Check the seasoning for salt and pepper and the aïoli is ready to use.

- A good tablespoon of mashed potato whizzed in with the aïoli makes an excellent addition.

METHOD: VELOUTÉ OF MUSSELS

- Drain the mussels in a colander then leave under cold, running water for a few minutes to get rid of the flour (see intro). Heat a large pan over a high heat until hot. Quickly throw in the mussels and the white wine. Cover and cook over a high heat, shaking the pan till all the mussels have opened. Drain them into a large colander, placed over a bowl to catch the cooking liquor.

- Once the mussels are cool enough to handle, remove them from the shells and set them aside in a bowl, discarding any that have not opened. Strain the cooking liquor through a muslin cloth into a bowl and reserve.

- In another saucepan, melt the butter, then sweat the onion until soft. Stir in the flour and curry powder, then cook gently for a few minutes. Add the cooking liquor from the mussels and stock, stir well and simmer for 10 minutes.

- Stir in the cream, bring back to the boil and add the mussels to warm them through. Finally, just before serving, add the spinach and ladle the soup into warmed bowls. Sprinkle liberally with snipped chives and a good dollop of aïoli in the soup. Serve with crusty bread.

LEEK & SAFFRON SOUP

Simple to make and very delicious. This recipe contains a classic saffron-and-leeks flavour combination. Back in the Medieval period, dishes like this would have been more of a hearty pottage, with cabbage or kale leaves, and pearl barley or cooked wheat grains added for bulk.

INGREDIENTS FOR 4 SERVINGS

500g (1 lb 2oz) leeks, quartered lengthways and finely chopped
50g (2oz) butter
1 tbsp olive oil
2 tbsp plain flour
20 saffron threads
1 litre (2 pts) chicken stock
salt and pepper

METHOD

- Grind the saffron in a pestle & mortar, add a little of the stock and infuse for at least 20 minutes.

- Cook the chopped leeks in the butter and oil for a few minutes.

- Remove from the heat and stir in the flour.

- Gradually stir in the stock and saffron infusion, then simmer for around 10 minutes or until the soup thickens and the leeks are cooked. Season with salt and pepper.

- The soup can then be served as it is or alternatively, whizz the soup with a hand-held blender until smooth before serving.

SAFFRON BUTTER SAUCE

From Carla Philips, a well-known cook in North Norfolk and ex-chef of a once famous restaurant. She writes, 'this sauce goes well with fettucine or other noodles, mixed with leftover shellfish, fish or chicken, and cooked peas.'

INGREDIENTS

a pinch of saffron threads
2 tbsp minced shallots
2 tbsp white wine vinegar
3 tbsp white wine
180-200g butter, very cold, cut into pieces
salt and pepper

METHOD

- Simmer the saffron, shallots, vinegar and wine until the mixture is reduced to about 1½ tbsp, then reduce the heat.

- Very, very gradually add in the cold butter. Lift the pan from the heat occasionally to cool the mixture and preserve the emulsification.

- Season with salt and pepper.

SAFFRON RISOTTO

It was the idea of Gianni Cestaro, father of one of my daughter's school friends, to include this recipe. This is, in essence, a simplified version of Risotto alla Milanese – one of the world's classic saffron dishes.

INGREDIENTS FOR 4 SERVINGS

30 saffron threads
1 litre (2pts) chicken stock
75g (3oz) butter
1 large onion, finely chopped
300g (12oz) arborio rice
50g (2oz) freshly-grated Parmesan cheese
salt and pepper

METHOD

• Grind the saffron in a pestle & mortar, add a little of the stock and infuse for at least 20 minutes. Mix with the remaining stock.

• Gently fry the onion in half of the butter until golden.

• Add the rice and stir to coat in the melted butter.

• Add the hot saffron stock a little at a time, stirring constantly until it has been absorbed; then add more saffron stock and repeat.

• When all the stock has been absorbed by the rice (after about 25 minutes of cooking), mix in the rest of the butter and the Parmesan. Season and serve very hot.

SAFFRON HADDOCK

Adapted from a medieval recipe, this comes from a great source of really interesting saffron dishes, *The Essential Saffron Companion* by John Humphries (Grub Street: 1996).

INGREDIENTS FOR 2 SERVINGS

30 saffron threads
1 very large glass dry white wine
2 tsp English mustard powder mixed with a splash of water
salt and pepper
a little oil
2 natural smoked haddock fillets
a knob of butter

METHOD

- Infuse the saffron threads in 2 tbsp of the white wine for 20 minutes.

- Mix together the rest of the wine, mustard, water, salt and pepper.

- In an ovenproof pan, heat the oil and briefly fry the haddock. Pour in the wine mixture and saffron infusion, bubbling together for one minute. Then put the pan into a hot oven for 10 minutes.

- When the haddock is cooked, reserve on a warm plate.

- Return the pan to the heat to reduce cooking juices; add a knob of butter so the sauce binds. It will become rich and delicious. Pour over the haddock and serve with mashed potato.

SEARED SEA BASS WITH SAFFRON POTATOES, LOBSTER BISQUE AND NORFOLK SAMPHIRE

Contributed by Flying Kiwi chef Chris Coubrough, this recipe was created at The Crown Inn in East Rudham, Norfolk, by Chris and The Crown's Head Chef, Fred Archer. If you are not familiar with samphire, it's the green plant lying on the fish. Those not able to pick it from the wild can instead buy it from fishmongers during summer.

INGREDIENTS FOR 4 SERVINGS

BISQUE

lobster shells (left over from either
   1 lobster) or 3 or 4 crabs shells
1 tbsp oil
a knob of butter
3 shallots, roughly chopped
1 bulb of fennel, roughly chopped
1 carrot, grated
2 cloves of garlic
2 sprigs of thyme

2 bay leaves
1 star anise
2 strips of orange peel (peeled with
a potato peeler)
1 tin chopped tomatoes
500ml fish stock
125ml white wine
100ml orange juice
50ml Pernod

SAFFRON POTATOES, SAMPHIRE & SEA BASS

20 new potatoes, peeled
¼ g saffron threads *
300g Norfolk samphire, washed
4 sea bass fillets, trimmed and scored

½ a lemon
1 tsp oil
knob of butter
salt and pepper

METHOD: BISQUE

- Heat the oil in a heavy bottom pan on a medium heat and add the star anise, bay leaves and orange peel.

- Fry for 1 minute then add the shallots, thyme, fennel, carrot and garlic with a knob of butter.

- Roast the lobster or crab shells in the oven for 10 minutes. Crush the roasted shells with a rolling pin and add to the pan, raise the heat for 1 minute and add the Pernod.

- With a lighter or match burn off the alcohol; this enhances the flavours.

- Add the wine and reduce for 5 minutes.

- Add the chopped tomatoes, orange juice and fish stock. Cook out on a low heat for 1 hour then strain through a sieve.

METHOD: SAFFRON POTATOES, SAMPHIRE & SEA BASS

- Peel the new potatoes and in a small pan just cover with water. Add the saffron threads, season with salt and cook for 20 minutes or until just soft. The potatoes should take on the colour and flavour of the saffron.

- Pick the samphire 'leaves' and blanch in a pan of non-salted water (samphire is naturally salty) for 2 minutes. Refresh in ice water.

- Score the sea bass diagonally across the skin about 2mm deep, 5 or 6 cuts per fillet, and season the flesh side with sea salt and freshly ground black pepper. Put a non-stick pan on medium/high heat with a teaspoon of oil. Just before the oil starts to smoke, seal the bass skin side down and gently push on the fish with your fingers or a plastic spatula, to stop the fillets curling.

- When the edges of the fish just start to golden, add a generous knob of butter, wait a second for it to foam and then squeeze over half a lemon. Baste the fish continuously by spooning over the lemon butter; if necessary finish the fish under a grill or in the oven but you do not need to turn the fish over until you serve.

- To complete the dish, arrange five saffron potatoes in a serving bowl or deep pasta plate. Put a heap of samphire in the middle then pour in enough hot bisque to cover and lay the sea bass skin side up across the middle. You can dust the rims of the bowls with smoked paprika and garnish with a lemon wedge.

*The saffron in the original recipe is whole threads. If, instead, the saffron is first ground before adding to the recipe, the quantity may be reduced.

SAFFRON COUS COUS

By Carla Philips. She writes, 'This famous North African dish, a casserole of vegetables enhanced with a little meat, benefits hugely from the small amount of saffron required. Even though there are a lot of ingredients, the actual preparation of this dish does not require mountains of work. This is truly a feast, and should be enjoyed by all present.'

INGREDIENTS FOR 4-6 SERVINGS

4-6 slices of scrag end of lamb
a full teacup of dried chickpeas
1 medium onion, roughly chopped
1 leek, sliced
1 clove of garlic
1 large carrot, sliced
1 medium turnip, roughly chopped
2 red or green peppers, sliced
2 large tomatoes, peeled and
   roughly chopped
2 or 3 chunks of white cabbage,
   roughly chopped
2 or 3 courgettes, or chunks of
   squash, sliced

a handful of sultanas
a handful of chopped coriander
2 bay leaves
1 tsp of cumin
2-3 peppercorns
1 tsp ground cinnamon
½ tsp ground ginger
12 saffron threads
1 tsp paprika
1-2 teaspoons salt
a packet of couscous
1-2 tsp harissa
Optional: a small amount of lamb
   sausage (merguez)

METHOD

- The day before, soak the dried chickpeas in plenty of cold water. Then, 3-4 hours before serving, drain the chickpeas and combine them with the scrag ends of lamb, onion, garlic, bay leaves, peppercorns and cumin and about 10-12cm (4-5 inches) of water to cover. Bring this to the boil, then lower the heat and leave for an hour.

- Next add the leek, carrot and turnip along with the ginger and cinnamon. Cook for another 30 minutes and add the saffron, paprika, peppers, cabbage and tomatoes as well as a teaspoon of salt.

- Cook for another 20 minutes, then add the sultanas, courgettes and coriander.

- After 20 minutes taste and add more salt if needed.

- Prepare sufficient couscous for 4-6 servings according to the packet's instructions, and cook the lamb sausage if you've got some.

- When ready to serve, spread the cooked couscous on a large, warmed serving dish. Chop the sausage into small pieces and scatter it over. Then, using a slotted spoon, cover the grains with the meat and vegetable mixture, adding a little of the broth. Roughly strain out some of this broth, and add a few teaspoons of harissa. Place this sauce in a separate jug, so that the diners can help themselves.

Grinding the saffron in a pestle and mortar makes the saffron go much further.

POULET DU GÂTINAIS

The Gâtinais was a saffron-producing area in France, into which the crop has now been re-introduced commercially. This is a traditional dish from that area, adapted from *Saffron: The Gold of Cuisine* (Agnès Viénot Éditions: 2008) by Jean Thiercelin.

INGREDIENTS FOR 4 SERVINGS

¼ g saffron threads
25g butter
100g oil
1 free range chicken, cut into pieces
3 large onions
1 bouquet garni (thyme, bay leaf and parsley)
chicken stock (ideally made from the chicken bones)

METHOD

- Grind the saffron in a mortar and infuse in 2 tbsp of the stock for at least 20 minutes.

- Melt together the butter and oil. Brown the chicken pieces on both sides and add the onions. Sweat until lightly coloured, then add the chicken stock. Cook for 35 minutes on low heat.

- Transfer the chicken to a serving dish and reduce the stock until thickened, to make a sauce. Do not discard the onions.

- Serve the chicken with its sauce alongside rice or vegetables.

SAFFRON LAMB RACK WITH TABOULEH & HUMMUS

Another delicious recipe from Chris Coubrough and Fred Archer, Flying Kiwi Inns. Here, the rack of lamb is first partially cooked in a rich saffron and cardamom stock before being finished in the oven.

INGREDIENTS FOR 4 SERVINGS

LAMB & SAFFRON STOCK/GLAZE

1 whole rack of spring lamb (with 8 bones preferably), excess fat trimmed
½ g saffron threads *
1 cardamom pod
½ cup sugar

HUMMUS

400g tin of cooked chickpeas, drained
1 or 2 garlic cloves
1 tsp of smoked paprika
1 tsp ground cumin
75ml natural yogurt
1 tbsp tahini paste

TABOULEH

1 bunch of parsley, chopped
½ a bunch of mint, chopped
1 red bell pepper (capsicum), diced
1 lemon (juice and zest)
1 cup of bulgur wheat
olive oil
salt and pepper
caper berries and olives for garnish

METHOD: HUMMUS

- Blend all the ingredients together to a smooth purée and season with salt and pepper.

METHOD: LAMB & TABOULEH

- Make a simple saffron stock in a pan with the cardamom pod, saffron and about a litre of water.

- Portion the lamb into 2 rack segments; this will give you 4 portions.

- Bring the saffron stock to the boil, drop the lamb in, cover and take off the heat.

- Meanwhile, cook the bulgur wheat by pouring 1 cup of boiling water over it in a bowl, tightly cover it and leave to cool.

- Make the tabouleh. In a bowl mix the parsley, mint, pepper, lemon (juice and zest), bulgur wheat, a splash of olive oil and season with salt and pepper.

- Remove the lamb from the saffron stock, add half a cup of sugar to the pan and reduce on a high heat until it becomes syrupy (a saffron glaze).

- Seal the lamb on a chargrill or in a medium/high heat non-stick pan and finish in a hot oven for 4-5 minutes (for medium rare). Leave to rest.

- To finish, arrange the tabouleh on the plate with a ramekin of hummus. Slice the racks of lamb between the bones and lean them on the tabouleh. Garnish with caper berries, olives and the saffron glaze. Serve with warm pitta bread.

*The saffron in the original recipe is whole threads. If, instead, the saffron is first ground before adding to the recipe, the quantity may be reduced.

SAFFRON ICE CREAM

A second recipe from *The Essential Saffron Companion* by John Humphries (Grub Street: 1996), and one of my family's all time saffron favourites. Serve it on its own or with sliced strawberries.

INGREDIENTS

20 saffron threads*
600ml (1pt) full cream milk
200ml (7fl oz) double cream
140g (5oz) sugar
5 free-range egg yolks, as fresh as possible

METHOD

• Bring the milk and cream to the boil, add the saffron, remove from heat and leave to infuse overnight.

• The following morning, beat the egg yolks and sugar in a bowl till smooth and white. Pour in a little of the saffron infusion and beat again.

• Place the eggs mixture and the rest of the saffron infusion in a saucepan and cook at 87°C for 3 minutes. Alternatively, use a bain marie and gently cook until the mixture coats the spoon.

• Pass the mixture through a fine sieve, rescue the saffron threads* and return them to the mixture. Allow to cool. When cold, churn the mixture in an ice cream machine. Alternatively, chill in a bowl in the freezer, remove at 1 hour intervals and beat it until it has set.

* We grind the saffron in a mortar, adding a little of the milk and then pouring it into the milk and cream mixture. We don't try and rescue the saffron at the sieving step.

SAFFRON PANNACOTTA WITH POACHED PEACH & PEACH SORBET

This dessert was contributed by Michelin starred chef, Kevin Mangeolles, Neptune Restaurant with Rooms, Old Hunstanton, Norfolk. The saffron goes beautifully in the pannacotta and with the peaches, making a lovely summery dessert.

INGREDIENTS FOR 4 SERVINGS

150g milk
300g whipping cream
2g saffron * and ½ tsp icing sugar
   (ground in a pestle & mortar)
75g caster sugar
20g water

2½ leaves of gelatine soaked in
   cold water
7 peaches
500g hot water
300g sugar
1 star anise

To garnish: sprigs of basil

METHOD

* Add the saffron to the milk and cream and bring to the boil.

* Boil the caster sugar and water to 115°C, add to the saffron milk then add the gelatine, mix and allow to cool. When this pannacotta mixture has nearly set, pour into glasses.

* Blanch the peaches in boiling water and put into cold water to remove the skin. Place the blanched peaches in a pan with 500g hot water, 300g sugar and the star anise. Cook the peaches until soft and allow to cool. Slice 4 of the peaches into segments and place on top of the pannacotta.

* Blend the 3 remaining peaches with 300g of the cooking juice. Pour into an ice cream machine and make into sorbet. Scoop the sorbet on to the peach slices. Garnish with small sprigs of basil.

*We have successfully made this recipe for ourselves using 30 threads of Norfolk Saffron.

GOLDEN BREAD & BUTTER PUDDING

An old fashioned hot pudding, made even better by the addition of saffron.

INGREDIENTS FOR 6 SERVINGS

20 saffron threads
275ml milk
80ml double cream
grated lemon zest (from half a lemon)
50g caster sugar
3 free-range eggs

8 slices of buttered white bread,
    cut into triangles, crusts left on
50g currants
10g finely chopped candied peel
nutmeg

METHOD

- Grind the saffron in a mortar, add 1-2 tbsp of the milk and allow to infuse for at least 20 minutes.

- Place half of the buttered bread in a layer over the base of a well buttered one litre baking dish. Sprinkle with half the currants and all of the peel.

- Make another layer of bread on top, and sprinkle with the rest of the currants.

- Beat the eggs, and add to the milk, cream, lemon zest and saffron infusion. Add the sugar. Mix well and pour over the bread in the baking dish.

- Sprinkle with freshly-grated nutmeg (too much overpowers the saffron) and bake at 180°C for 30-40 minutes.

NORFOLK SAFFRON SHORTCAKES

Not to be confused with shortbread, Norfolk shortcakes were, and still are, made from the pastry trimmings left after a baking session. In 2009, a customer of ours said that her mother added saffron to shortcakes at Easter. This version is based on my great-grandmother's shortcakes method, but with added saffron.

INGREDIENTS FOR ABOUT 15

150g (6oz) plain flour
75g (3oz) fat (traditionally half butter
and half lard, but can be all butter)
12 saffron threads
25g (1oz) currants
granulated sugar
milk

METHOD

- Crush the saffron threads and infuse in about 4 tbsp hot water for at least 30 minutes; allow to cool fully.

- Rub the fat into the flour, and add the saffron water to make the pastry dough.

- Roll out and brush half the pastry with milk, sprinkle with sugar and half of the currants. Fold over and roll out again.

- Repeat, using the remainder of the currants. Fold and roll out as before.

- Finally, mark into 4 x 5cm rectangles, decorate the top in a criss-cross diamond pattern, brush with milk and sprinkle with sugar.

- Bake at 160°C, for 15 minutes.

- The saffron-enriched pastry can be used for sweet, dessert pies instead of being made into shortcakes.

NORFOLK SAFFRON, CARDAMOM & GOLD MACARONS

Masterchef finalist and king of macarons Dr Tim Kinnaird (Macarons and More) provided this mouth-watering recipe. Tim is based in Norfolk and attends (amongst others) our local Farmers' Market, at North Creake Abbey, Norfolk.

INGREDIENTS

SAFFRON MACARON SHELLS

200g icing sugar
200g caster sugar
200g ground almonds
100g egg white

large pinch of saffron
35ml water
optional: edible gold lustre

CARDAMOM & WHITE CHOCOLATE GANACHE

250g white chocolate
110g double cream
8 cardamom pods

METHOD

- Pre-heat the oven to 150°C.

- Crush the cardamom pods to release the seeds and place the pods and seeds in a pan with the cream. Heat the cream to just boiling and then turn off the heat and leave to infuse for at least 30 minutes. Break the chocolate into chunks and melt in a bain-marie. Pass the cream through a sieve onto the melted chocolate and combine to produce a smooth ganache. Allow to cool at room temperature.

- Add the saffron to 1 tablespoon of warm water and leave it to infuse into the water for 5 minutes. Mix this with 50g of the egg white, the icing sugar and the ground almonds. Beat this mixture until well combined.

- Place the remaining 50g of egg white in the bowl of a free-standing mixer. Heat the caster sugar and the water in a pan to make a sugar syrup. When the mixture reaches 114°C turn on the mixer to whisk the egg whites. When the sugar syrup has reached 118°C pour it onto the whisking egg whites. Continue to whisk until the meringue has formed stiff peaks.

- Fold the meringue into the almond and icing sugar mix. Mix until the meringue is incorporated and it forms ribbons when dropped from the spoon into the bowl. The mixture should flow like lava!

- Place the batter into a piping bag with a plain round 1cm nozzle. Pipe small rounds approximately 2.5cm in diameter onto baking parchment lined trays. Dust the shells with edible gold lustre.

- Place the macaron shells into the oven and turn the heat down to zero. After 8 minutes turn the heat back up to 150°C for a further 8 minutes. Allow the shells to cool.

- The cardamom ganache needs to be thick enough to pipe onto the shells. If the ganache is runny it can be placed in the fridge but be careful as it will easily set hard. Sandwich two shells together.

- The macarons are best eaten after 24 hours in the fridge but they should be brought back up to room temperature before eating.

SAFFRON-ICED SAFFRON BUNS

Saffron cookery doesn't get much easier than this! These buns are much loved by my daughter.

INGREDIENTS

BUNS

100g (4oz) self-raising flour
100g (4oz) caster sugar
100g (4oz) soft margarine
2 free-range eggs
12 saffron threads

SAFFRON ICING

5 heaped tbsp icing sugar
9 saffron threads

METHOD

- Crush the 12 threads of saffron and infuse in 1 tbsp boiling water for 20 minutes.

- Beat together all the other bun ingredients and mix the saffron infusion into the bun mixture. Spoon the mixture into bun cases and cook for 15 minutes at 180°C.

- Whilst the buns are cooling, steep the 9 crushed threads of saffron in 2 tsp boiling water for 20 minutes, then strain through a seive. Sift the icing sugar into a bowl and mix in the strained saffron infusion (plus more water if required, adding it a teaspoon-full at a time) until smooth. Ice the buns.

SLEMP (DUTCH SAFFRON MILK)

Such a lot of Norfolk's saffron was exported to the Netherlands historically, it seemed right to include at least one Dutch recipe. Dutch Saffron Milk, or Slemp, was the suggestion of a charming Dutch man we met in Norwich at our Norfolk Saffron stall recently. Slemp is a traditional drink, served in winter.

INGREDIENTS FOR 6 SERVINGS

1 litre full cream milk
20 saffron threads, ground
    in a pestle & mortar
2 tsp tea leaves
2 strips of lemon peel (removed
    using a potato peeler)
1 cinnamon stick, 10cm long

1 blade mace
2 cloves
40g sugar
3 egg yolks or 1 yolk plus
    1 tsp cornflour
nutmeg

METHOD

• Grind the saffron in the mortar, add 1-2 tbsp of the milk and infuse for at least 20 minutes.

• Bring the rest of the milk to a simmer, then remove from the heat.

• Place tea leaves in an infuser, and steep this, the lemon zest, cinnamon, mace and cloves in the hot milk. Add the saffron infusion. After 1 hour, remove the infuser, strain out the spices, then mix in the sugar.

• Beat the egg yolks (or yolk plus cornflour), add a little of the warm milk then pour back into the saucepan.

• Constantly stirring, gently heat the mixture until it thickens.

• Serve hot in heat-resistant glasses. Sprinkle freshly-grated nutmeg on top.

GENEVA ROLLS

This recipe is a simplified version of the Victorian original, a kind of white roll subtly flavoured with saffron. These rolls are lovely split and toasted for Sunday morning breakfast.

INGREDIENTS FOR ABOUT 16 ROLLS

20-30 saffron threads
1 kg strong white flour
75g butter, cut into small pieces
500ml milk, warmed

100ml warm water
2 tsp salt
3 tsp fast action yeast
1 free-range egg, beaten

METHOD

• Crumble the saffron threads into milk and allow to infuse for at least 20 mins.

• Rub the butter into the flour, then mix in the salt and yeast.

• Make up the dough using the saffron infusion and warm water. Knead until the dough is smooth and elastic. Set aside to prove for 1 hour, or until the dough has doubled in volume.

• Form the dough into rolls. Place them on a greased baking sheet approximately 2cm apart. Cover with a clean tea towel.

• When the rolls are nearly touching each other, begin pre-heating the oven to 220°C.

• When the rolls just begin to touch each other, carefully brush them with the beaten egg and bake for 15-20 minutes or until done.

Storing your saffron
After making these delicious recipes, store any remaining saffron in a tightly-closed container in the dark, in a cool, dry place away from strong odours.

NOTES

GLOSSARY

Carotenoid – *one of a group of yellow, orange or red plant-derived pigments sharing a similar chemical structure.*

Corm – *often called a bulb, but corms are significantly different. A corm (e.g. of a crocus) is a short, swollen, underground stem of solid tissue, whilst a bulb (e.g. of a daffodil or an onion) is a thickened shoot made of distinct layers (scale leaves).*

Croker – *the traditional English name for a saffron grower. In France the much more glamorous sounding Safranier is used!*

Filament – *the stalk part of a stamen (of which, see).*

Hybrid – *an individual produced from genetically different parents.*

Infusion – *a solution made by steeping a spice or herb in hot water.*

Stamen – *the male part of a flower. It comprises the filament and the anther (which produces pollen).*

Stigma – *receptive surface of the female organ of a flower, on which pollen grains germinate during pollination.*

Style – *part of the female organs of a flower in between the stigma and the ovary (in which the seed develops).*

PICTURE CREDITS

Pages: 7 & 12 (left), Banco de Germoplasma Vegetal de Cuenca (Junta de Comunidades de Castilla – La Mancha, Spain);

12 (right) & 13, Steve Blacksmith;

10 & 42, Österreichische Nationalbibliothek (Wien, Austria);

21 (top), Norfolk Record Office;

21 (bottom), Dr Jenny Aitken;

25, Saffron Walden Museum;

28, Prof José Antonio Fernandez (original photographer, Maria A. Serrano);

37, Kentwell Hall, Suffolk (original photographer, Andrew Howarth);

48, Dulwich Picture Gallery;

50 (bottom) & 51, Aviva Leigh;

53, Kevin Mangeolles;

62 & 68, Chris Coubrough (original photographer, Keiron Trovell);

76, Dr Tim Kinnaird.

All other images and artwork © Sally Francis.

INDEX